"Shahnaz Husain has b

lifet

Ingrid Bergman

"Internationally famous—she is an established
name in Skin and Hair care."

The New York Times

"She is spreading the rich herbal heritage of India
around the world."

Guardian

"The jet age beauty tycoon."

The Mirror, UK

"Fabulous and fascinating."

Barbara Cartland, London

"The uncrowned queen of India's beauty
industry.... Shahnaz Husain is as exotic as her
name."

Daily Telegraph, UK

"Shahnaz Husain is god's gift to the world. Her sole purpose in life is to make other people's life more beautiful and worth living."

Black Beauty, London, UK

"A guru of gorgeousness—Shahnaz Husain exudes an aura of herbal confidence—stemming from years of research and dedication".

Miss London, UK

"Shahnaz Husain's knowledge in the field of herbal cures is unparalleled. She has become an institution in herself, at an International level'.

Nina Haas, President CIDESCO International, Monte Carlo

"Shahnaz Husain has taken the world by storm by going back to nature..."

Saudi Gazette, Jeddah, Saudi Arabia

"Shahnaz Husain has done for India's image what no one in that country has been able to do by way of promoting India's image abroad in cosmetics."

Beauty Salon, UK

Shahnaz Husain's
BEAUTY BOOK

Orient Paperbacks
DELHI | MUMBAI | HYDERABAD

Everyone has a god they worship — I had mine — my
father. I worshipped him — he taught me to have total
faith in my limitless capabilities. He always said you make
your own destiny — your life will be exactly the way you
will it to be.

This book I dedicate to his undying memory.

— *Shahnaz Husain*

www.orientpaperbacks.com

ISBN 13: 978-81-222-0060-5
ISBN 10: 81-222-0060-5

1st Published 1991
18th Printing 2010

Shahnaz Husain's Beauty Book

© Shahnaz Husain

Illustrated by Neelam Taneja

Photography by Kitty Hazuria

Published by
Orient Paperbacks
(A Division of Vision Books Pvt. Ltd.)
5A/8 Ansari Road, New Delhi-110 002

Printed in India at
Ravindra Printing Press, Delhi-110 006

Contents

INTRODUCTION

I have always believed that in life it is not what you want that is important. What really matters is how badly you want it. It is possible to achieve just about everything in life. What is necessary is total dedication, honesty and loyalty to your values. I was only fourteen when I was engaged and at fifteen I was married. It was an ideal, arranged match. Before my sixteenth birthday, I was the mother of a beautiful baby girl. Then the mental upheaval began. I was in search of something. Life seemed too perfect, but I was bored with the drudgery of endless routine. Today apparently, I have everything I can ask for, nothing more. I never planned it this way... my success has far exceeded its dreams. When I returned to India, after schooling in those famous beauty houses from Helena Rubinstine to Christine Valmay, I had seen the ill effects of synthetics and their irreversible side effects and decided that I would go back to my country and try and find a natural alternative. In fact, whenever I have looked towards nature, I have been able to find a better answer.... I worked out all those fabled formulas. Rather than entering the market, I thought I would have a small exclusive clinic, where my clients would only use my custom-made products. I borrowed 35 thousand rupees from my father... that is how I began.

A decade ago, skin and hair treatments, from the aspect of cures, were relatively unknown. Superficial beauty treatments or hair styling were 'treats' women went in for without realising that beauty is the outcome of long term and life long care. I was determined to increase this awareness amongst women that the beauty of the skin and hair depend on their health, that diets and habits, climatic factors are important in beauty care—and the treatments and cosmetics suited to white skins may not be the answer to our problems. I also knew that India has a vast store house of tried and trusted herbal remedies which could be applied to beauty. So I started propagating the use of herbs. I changed all my magic formulas into reality... into herbal creams, lotions, powders, packs, cures and remedies. And today, the wheel has turned a full circle... herbs are 'in' all over the world and people are turning away from synthetic products to natural ones.

It is my approach to beauty therapy that is responsible for our rapid expansion into a world-wide chain of herbal clinics. I believe that the external condition of the skin and hair is directly related to the internal body condition and vice-versa. When I finally came back to India, I had never intended to enter the 'across-the-counter' race, where salesmen sell brand names to unknown, faceless customers. Instead, I opened a clinic and geared my herbal formulas to the cure of specific problems. I also started a beauty school and found that the ultimate dream of every student was to open a clinic on the lines of Shahnaz Herbal. I encouraged the average housewife to open a clinic in her own house, so that she could persue a career and also be at hand to take care of her domestic responsibilities. Under my franchise system, I have given them the right to open Shahnaz Herbal Clinics. Thus, today we have branched out into almost every suburb and town in India and several abroad.

I have always put certain human values before everything else and I attribute a major part of my success to this. I treat each client as an individual and try to establish a kind of emotional rapport with her. My treatments are considered expensive by those who can afford them. For those who cannot, they are free. A woman must only have the desire to be beautiful, to be cured. I place no importance on the relationship between her need for treatment and her ability to pay for it. They are two separate issues. The desire to be beautiful is innate in every human being and I respect and understand it. My slogan was always, "if you can pay—pay,—if you can't, then pray"—the policy paid heavy spiritual dividends. Over the years, I have built up a spiritual liaison with my clients and their goodwill has reflected on me. When the client leaves the clinic, she is not forgotten. We have a massive feedback programme. We also maintain a clinical system of client cards, where each individual's personal data is recorded, including past and present treatments, specific allergies, sensitivities, skin and hair types etc. I think it is this kind of personalised technique which has enabled my clients to establish a personal rapport with my herbal chain.

Today there are numerous beauticians who may be finding the beauty business very lucrative, but they seem to be quite content within the walls of their parlour. They have never tried to venture beyond them to find a place for India on the international scene. India, with her vast herbal heritage, should have found her place on the beauty map of the world long ago. So during my trips abroad to attend Beauty Congresses, I tried to crusade Indian herbal remedies. I propagated their use in New York when I represented India at the CIDESCO Congress. (India was represented for the first time in the 34 years history of the Congress). Appointed President of the day's proceedings, I took the opportunity to direct world focus on herbal cosmetics, high-lighting the immense scope of Indian herbal remedies in the International Cosmetic Market. I pointed out that there was no reason why herbal cosmetics manufactured in India should not find a prominent place in international stores, with their therapeutic values and element of safety. In a world that is looking towards nature with enlightened eyes, my claims generated a great deal of interest and several lucrative offers of collaboration from foreign beauty houses came my way. But I stuck to my guns, and my solo Indian image.

My husband is an essential part of my meteoric rise. In fact, my success is closely linked with him, that without him, I would cease to exist. Without his constant support, encouragement and understanding, I would never have achieved what I have. He has become an integral part of my life and work and I need and value his advice. I feel very secure when he is present. . . . that nothing can go wrong when he is making the decision. I also owe a lot to my father for his encouragement for goading me on and making me believe in myself and my abilities. On his advice, I opened SHAMUTE—a free Beauty Institute for deaf and dumb girls. I will never forget what my father said, "My child, how can you feed the mind and starve the soul. The way you require food to live, the soul requires spiritual food. . . . you are living a batteried existence. . . . you must prepare yourself for life after death." And Shamute was born.

Early motherhood had its advantages. My daughter, Nelofar, and I grew up together, like two sisters. We went to a beauty school together in London, and it was fun. There is nothing more beautiful than growing up with your own child. She became an integral part of my 'Beautiful World' and as time went on and I started attending International Beauty Congress, she would fly with me to Paris, New York, or London, in her personal capacity as a beauty therapist. She is married and life is still beautiful. I am a grandmother now and I think it is wonderful to cuddle your baby's baby. I hear people remark: "But you don't look like a grandmother". I am not sure what a grandmother should look like, but it has not changed me in any way—except giving me the perfect joy of knowing that Nelofar is married to Tabrik, the most wonderful boy in the whole world and they have two baby boys, Sharik and Zubeck.

I am often faced with the question—After you—what? An entire business, especially one that has been built on the charisma and the personal efforts of one person, has been known to collapse with the loss of the binding force—but, I have groomed my daughter in such a way that she should have no difficulty in stepping into my role. When I became a career woman, I dreamt of the day when Nelofar would have a career too. I taught her to value 'time' and to live each day as if it was a separate, complete life. Today, she is a complete person in her own right—the way I had wanted her to be. She is my dream come true, my Nelofar. . . . the natural successor to my herbal chain, schooled at some of the best cosmetic centres in the world. I have trained her with meticulous care, so that when the burden finally falls on her, she will hold together with pride and courage, the Beautiful World I have built and left for her to perpetuate.

I have often been told that I am fortunate to be so successful—that my life is so obviously perfect. But, I know that in skimming on the waves of success, I may have missed out on the finer values of life—like spending time with my little son Samir who is twelve. I often feel that in my efforts to be a perfect career woman, I am failing as the perfect mother and the perfect wife. My son and grandsons will grow into handsome young men, I am sure, but I will never really enjoy their fleeting childhoods, because my commitments are so different. There are my clients who need me, an ornate room, soft music, promises and cures, worshipping eyes and endless hope—the telephone ringing and the intercom buzzings, often simultaneously. There is where I belong. The clients are waiting for me. That is my Beautiful World. My scene-

What am I to say to them? Can I say that I cannot attend to them because my son needs the warmth of his mother and cries coming home from school to an empty house. I know that I have to forget my personal commitments and go to them. I push my emotions, my problems and tensions to the back of my mind. I smile at them, their eyes full of faith and confidence, and try to make their visits worthwhile. Like a Mecca of cure—they converge from every corner of the world to this shrine of hope. It is they who have made my dream come true. I had dreams of establishing a 'Beauty Chain'.... today the largest chain of its kind in the world...who says, "dreams remain dreams?" Much more than I ever dreamt has come true.

Shahnaz Husain

HERBAL HERITAGE

Nature—The Expert Cosmetologist

NATURE is not only a cosmetologist, but an expert chemist! She has provided such versatile natural ingredients that enhance the beauty of the skin and hair and have amazing curative properties. The body's response to organic substances is extremely good and there is the advantage of protection from chemical after-effects and irritative reactions. These ingredients may even be categorised under familiar cosmetological terms..... like cleansers, tonics, nourishers, fresheners, astringents, moisturisers, humectants and so on. In fact, an entire range of cosmetic products exists in nature!

Plant and herbal extracts, essential oils and tinctures have several benefits as cosmetic applications. Some have nourishing or cleansing actions, some whip up the circulation, others refine the pores, while some freshen the skin, leaving it soft and glowing. Many promote the skin's capacity to absorb, thus allowing better penetration of the product applied. Natural ingredients have preventive, protective and even corrective actions. Apart from the curative aspect, herbal cosmetic aids are ideal for maintaining the health of the skin and hair.

Sandalwood, eucalyptus, clove, comfrey, camphor, arnica are antiseptic and germicidal agents, yet, soothe the skin. They have been formulated into creams and ointments to heal inflammatory conditions of the skin. Sandalwood creams protect the skin against sun damage and control acne conditions, soothing clove packs have benefited sensitive skin conditions. Some of these extracts have the ability to cleanse the skin, without any harsh effect.

Many herbs contain emollient substances, which keep the skin texture soft and smooth. Others provide excellent nourishment. Camomile is an emollient plant. Cabbage, carrot, almond, date, apricot, etc., have been included in nourishing creams as they are 'skin foods', with high vitamin and mineral contents. Such creams have been used to rejuvenate the skin, improve skin tone and elasticity and minimise wrinkling. Extracts of cactus and aloe have been used to rehydrate the skin. Many herbal products are not only excellent moisturisers, but also prevent moisture loss. In other words, they are natural humectants.

Skin problems arise out of imbalances in the acid-alkaline or the oil-moisture contents of the skin. This is also true of hair disorders, the scalp being an extension of the skin. When we use harsh cleansers, we upset the natural acid-alkaline balance, or cause a depletion of moisture. Herbal extracts and many natural substances like turmeric, shikakai, henna, reetha, lemon, egg white, yoghurt have powerful cleansing actions. Plant products contain natural enzymes which help to cleanse the skin of dead cells. At the same time, they prevent imbalances or even correct them. Thus, the good health of the skin is ensured. Extracts of rose have been included in skin tonics for oily skins, removing impurities, refining the texture and improving skin tone. Ginseng, used by the ancient Chinese, is an ideal skin cleanser, for its moisturising ability. It also achieves the right balance between oil and moisture.

Not only does Nature have a range so flexible, but there is a variety of products to choose from. Experiments have shown that these can be adapted very successfully to modern demands, in ready-to-use, bottled forms, with longer shelf life. Some natural ingredients are actually preservatives, while others are hardening agents, which can be used as bases for face masks. Many are excellent emulsifiers. Not only that, fruits, vegetables and other herbal extracts and oils have their own delicious aromas and fragrances. These qualities have allowed the manufacture of cosmetics that are truly natural, without any synthetic perfumes and preservatives.

Indian Herbal Heritage

WE know only too well that from ancient times our women have been borrowing from nature's bounty to care for their skin and hair. These ancient recipes, which are part of our vast Indian herbal heritage, have not only stood the test of time, but have been most beneficial in counter-acting the harmful effects of synthetic and chemical preparations.

The modern method of using *turmeric* in creams is based on the ancient Indian germicidal treatment and skin softening remedy. Turmeric combined with lemon, into a pre-bath gel is an ideal way of ensuring softness and smoothness of the skin, as well as cleansing it thoroughly. It also forms a screen between the skin and the dehydrating effects of soap and water washing.

Ancient Indian women used this combination for its gentle depilating action on the skin. Applying turmeric on the body is still a part of traditional Indian weddings when the bride is beautified for the ceremony.

Honey is a powerful natural moisturiser. It prevents moisture loss from the skin and also supplies moisture to it. Honey can be used in cream form, or as a pack, with apricot. This combination, used as a peel-off pack is ideal for porcelaining the skin, closing the pores and discouraging facial hair. Both apricot and honey have a most beneficial effect on the skin, by softening it and adding a glow.

A herbal product, popular in the West, is *thyme*. It has antiseptic qualities and is used in acne treatments. The famed Indian rosewater is an astringent, used for closing the pores and toning the skin. Used regularly, it helps to slow down the ageing process of the skin.

Lemongrass is being exported from India for therapeutic reasons. In ancient India it was used for treating open pores and pimples. Similarly, *lavender* and *jasmine* have long been used in India, in combination with the *oil of black rose* and *Fuller's earth*, as a pack for tightening the skin on the face and body.

Even the common hair removing agent known as wax, which is a *sugar* and *lemon* mixture, has its basis in the ancient Indian Herbal heritage. Numerous instances have been found of Indian women making use of herbs for their therapeutic benefits. So much so, that today a combination of *ivory* powder and oil from the *marigold* flower is being tried as a cure for leucoderma.

Gram flour and *wheat husk* are still used as a method of cleaning the skin. It is an accepted fact that washing with soap and water accelerates the ageing process of the skin because it washes away the natural oils and removes the protective mantle of the skin.

Interestingly enough, in India, soap has never been regarded as a beauty aid. Indian women find it more beneficial to use gram flour or wheat husk, mixed with milk, to clean their skins. Wheat husk has a gentle derm-abrasive effect on the skin, cleansing it of dead epithelial cells, leaving it cleaner and brighter.

There is another ancient method which involves rubbing the body with a mixture of *starch, cream* and *husk*. The starch tightens the skin, the cream provides the nourishment and the husk removes the dead skin cells. The body is then rinsed with water in which rose petals have been soaked overnight. This leaves the skin clear, smooth and perfumed. Costing a fortune in fabled salons, these treatments have roots deeply embedded in the Indian beauty heritage.

Ancient Indian women are always envied for their thick lustrous hair. They owed their beauty to natural aids, like *shikakai* and *reetha* for washing their hair. Both these herbal products are natural cleansing agents, without the harmful effects of the detergents contained in all shampoos.

Amla, the Indian gooseberry, has hair-darkening properties and forms the basis of many herbal hair oils.

To us Indians, *henna* treatment for the hair is as old as history. In the West, henna hair conditioners and henna shampoos are making big news. This fad has its basis in the ancient hair-dye method of gradually converting whitening hair to a brown colour.

When henna powder is combined with *yoghurt, egg* and *lemon juice* and applied to the hair, it is known to accelerate hair growth and is used in treating cases of falling hair and alopecia. Henna is also a powerful anti-dandruff agent.

Indian women have also been using boiled and strained water from used *tea leaves*, with lemon juice, for treating their hair and imparting a glossy look to it.

Probably the most far-reaching and significant effects can be seen in the use of herbs in the treatment of various skin and hair problems, i.e. herbs viewed from the curative aspect.

Apart from their proved therapeutic values, the fact which cannot be ignored is that in many cases, the risks of surgery or chemical products are avoided. For instance, in the treatment of facial scars, resulting from acne, injuries, even smallpox, herbal products have been used with success. The time involved depends on the extent of scarring.

Several items from the kitchen can be used as beauty aids.

Milk can be applied on the scalp and hair for nourishment, especially in cases of dry, brittle or damaged hair. It is a completely natural treatment, without any synthetic or chemical additives.

An egg can be used for the hair before a shampoo. Leave it on for about an hour and then wash the hair. Rinsing the hair thoroughly is important for that clean, healthy look. The egg can be used on the face too. The yolk contains vitamin and protein, while the white has skin-tightening and tissue-building properties.

Vegetables and *fruits* are a natural storehouse of beauty aids. *Potatoes* may not be good for the figure, but are known to be skin-cleaning agents. Rub the face gently with slices of raw potato or potato halves. They contain Vitamin C and are even known to benefit skin conditions like eczema. Potatoes also benefit the area around the eyes, relieving puffiness and making the eyes fresh and clear. *Cucumber juice* also benefits the area around the eyes, especially if there are dark circles.

Cotton wool pads can be soaked in cucumber juice and used as eye pads. What has proved to be one of the best treatmemts for this delicate region is a combination of *almond* and *lanolin*. This, in cream form, is an ideal treatment for the under-eyes, keeping them free of wrinkles and dark circles.

Our grandmothers used tea water to brighten their eyes. Modern women too can use tea bags as eye pads!

Most of us know *lemon* as a concentrate of Vitamin C and have taken it at some time or the other for the prevention of colds, to ward off thirst and, of course, to add some tangy spice to a food item. But do you know, that there's much more to the lemon's potential, both as a beauty and health food?

It increases the body resistance to infection. It has a strong anti-bacterial action. Its contents of glucose, mineral salts, calcium and iron gives it some fantastic properties. It is therefore recommended for good salad seasoning. It is also good for reducing weight.

Salads: Lemon is much better than vinegar in all cases of stomach or intestinal disorders, and for people suffering from nervous strain or anxiety. Dentists also advise against regular use of vinegar, as it has harmful effect on the teeth. It irritates the mucous membrane of the mouth and the digestive system.

Lemon stimulates blood circulation, reduces arterial pressures, activates bile and intestinal secretions and produces a general feeling of well being. However, remember that it is best taken diluted. Else, the acid it contains will irritate the gastric mucous membrane, resulting in stomach burns. It also adversely affects the tooth enamel in its neat form.

Start the day with lemon juice. A good morning combination is the juice of half a lemon and an orange, squeezed in a glass of hot water, sweetened with honey. This mix will ward off the harmful effects of the routine morning tea, flush the entire system and help to relieve constipation.

Even plain lemon juice taken with hot water is a good beginning to the day. It will lend a glow to the skin, keep gums healthy, ward off colds and add a sparkle to your eyes.

For obstinate intestines, try lemon juice in hot water, add prunes and a few raisins. Soak this overnight and take it first in the morning.

For weight watchers and those on a reducing programme, lemon is excellent. It has other beauty promises too. Since it helps in depigmentation of the skin, it is useful for those suffering from blemishes and blotchy skin.

Here are some other ways of using lemon as a beauty aid:

As a bleach: for elbows, heels and toes: Rub lemon halves on these areas and then rinse off.

As a hand lotion: Mix it with rose water and rub to smoothen hands. Rub granulated sugar and the juice of a lemon together till the sugar is dissolved. Then rinse off. Follow this treatment daily for a month.

As a hair rinse: Add lemon juice to boiled and strained tea water. Use immediately after the shampoo. It highlights dull hair, making it shine.

Miracle of Henna   *SHAHAIR SHACARE*

MUCH before the invention of chemical colourants as dyes, plant products were used to colour the hair, hands and nails. Among these, one of the best known is henna.

Our ancient counterparts may not have had the ease of ready-to-use beauty aids in bottled form. They had to go through the process of grinding and mixing. Little did they realise then, that the advantage they had was complete protection from the effects of chemical and synthetic substances.

Chemical irritations and after-reactions were unheard of and yet, their remedies achieved the desired results.

The use of henna has been traced back to ancient Egypt. It was used in the Middle East as well as in India. Henna, it is believed, originated as a cooling device, since it is reputed to have such an effect. The paste of henna leaves was applied to bring down high fevers and was used as an antidote against heat and sunstroke. This probably explains its extensive use in tropical countries. Gradually henna developed into a beauty aid, because of its versatility. In India, the application of henna in intricate designs on the palms and feet still exists as an important part of traditional weddings. In Egypt, as in India, women used henna to colour their nails, to beautify them the way we apply nail varnish.

The best results of henna have been seen in its use as a hair treatment, with an almost unending list of benefits. Apart from safety, the advantage that it has over chemical hair colourants is that it is also an excellent hair conditioner.

Chemical dyes can, in fact, damage the hair structure, while henna protects it. Henna has the ability of coating the hair shaft, thus conditioning and thickening the hair.

Henna applications add beauty, body and bounce to the hair, leaving it supple, shiny and easy to manage. It is also a very effective cleanser, both for the hair and scalp, and unlike detergents, does not destroy the natural acid nature of the scalp, which is a pre-requisite to healthy hair. Henna paste, mixed with lemon juice, egg and yoghurt, is probably one of the best known methods of cleansing and conditioning the hair. Regular use of this combination has been seen to promote hair growth and restore good health to the scalp.

The most apparent result of henna is, of course, its ability to colour the hair. A question that is commonly asked is if henna will turn the hair red. Since henna leaves a reddish colour, this question will apply to blond hair, but not to those with dark hair, either brown or black. Dark hair cannot turn red. Instead, henna will lend the hair beautiful coppery tints, which would highlight the hair, making it gleaming and lustrous.

The method of applying henna should be based on the desired effect. If it is to be used as a dye, add coffee to the henna paste to give it a rich brown colour. The paste should be kept on till it dries and then washed off.

Henna is known to check greying, if used regularly, but it will not turn hair that has already greyed to its original colour. When the grey hair is not much, henna can be used very effectively, as the grey hair will be dyed brown and blend with the rest of the dark hair.

However, when most of the hair has already turned grey, henna will give it a reddish colour. Most women with grey hair, therefore, turn to chemical dyes, without realising the damage they are actually doing to

Shahnaz Husain

*My daughter Nelofar, the natural successor
to my Beauty Business, schooled at some of
the best cosmetic centers in the world. I have
trained her with meticulous care, so that
when the burden finally falls on her, she will
hold together with pride and courage, the
Beautiful World, I built and left for her to
perpetuate.*

the texture and health of the hair. If you must dye your hair, you should give the hair a henna treatment about twice a month, as a protective measure.

Like many other plant products, the therapeutic value of henna has been put to use in the treatment of beauty problems associated with hair, like dandruff and hair loss. Not only does it promote the growth of hair, it also ensures healthy restoration of the scalp's acid mantle. This makes it an effective anti-dandruff agent.

In fact, the miraculous results achieved with henna have led to the formulation of specialised products containing henna, like shampoos and conditioning powders.

Together with henna, other ingredients like amla, shikakai, brahmi and lichens are added. The henna powder is in fact, a complete hair food treatment for making the hair healthy and lustrous. It also acts as a preventive measure against hair loss, scalp disorders and greying.

Cases of alopecia areata (patchy baldness) have been successfully treated with such specialised products. For a total conditioning and healing effect, the henna powder should be mixed in the following way: Henna—3 tablespoons, Yoghurt—200 gms, eggs—2, and the juice of one lemon. Two teaspoonfuls of coffee may be added, but this is optional.

Mix together into a paste and apply it evenly all over the head. The easiest way to apply henna is to divide the hair into sections with a comb, applying henna to each section. As you apply, wind each section around the head in the form of a large coil or chignon. This ensures that the henna is applied all over, right up to the roots. It is also easier to remove the henna. Leave on the paste for at least half an hour.

Whether it is health or beauty, prevention or cure, whichever way you view it, henna is indeed one of nature's many miracles. What is making 'cosmetic news' is not just new products, but an entirely new concept that will revolutionise skin-care and skin-care aids.

Cosmetics today must perform various functions: maintain the health and beauty of the skin, protect it from the dangers of harmful elements and prevent many problems. What deserves equal importance is that they provide cures to many skin problems that detract from beauty. This concept of 'cosmetics as cures' is certainly worth a second look.

INTRODUCING HERBS

NATURAL products, by Shahnaz Herbal, comprise the latest in skin and hair care techniques. The formulas are highly specialised and keep individual problems in view. They not only enhance the beauty of the skin, but are designed to deal with all skin and hair problems, like dryness, excessive oiliness, acne, blemishes, pigmentation, freckles, scars, premature ageing, lines, wrinkles, dandruff, falling/damaged hair, alopecia. Shahnaz Herbal products are the result of years of individual analysis and client demand—of custom blended herbal extracts from daily skin care programmes to specialised cures. Shahnaz Herbal products are a unique combination of tried, trusted herbal remedies and the latest developments in beauty science.

At the time when the world is riding on the crest of a herb wave, Shahnaz Herbal offers a range of about 50 different natural products, made from pure extracts of almond, cactus, aloe, lemon, rose, sandalwood, honey, apricot, henna, turmeric, cabbage, seaweed, etc., which are known for their healing and beautifying properties. Shahnaz Husain, the force behind Shahnaz Herbal, has devised an entire range of creams, lotions, moisturisers, masks and pastes, which reflect a deep understanding of different skin and hair problems in the context of modern-day life. For instance, sandalwood heal and conceal base is an ideal protective cream for all skin types, specially prepared to combat the pollution problem. There is also a range of special cleansers, rose extract skin tonics, and other medicated products. Face packs and masks are a speciality of Shahnaz Herbal, ranging from medicated face masks to herbal powders, to be combined with yoghurt, seaweed, honey and egg white. Ready to use masks, like the Apricot-Honey Peel-Off pack and Rexturising Protein Mask are a time-saving and pleasant route to beauty, closing the pores, ironing out lines and wrinkles and porcelaining the skin. Hair care products and cures, comprising herbal Hair Rinses, Tonics, Shampoos and Henna Powders, are designed to restore beauty and health to the hair. They contain extracts known for their qualities of simulating hair growth, improving hair texture and colour.

In the last decade, the name Shahnaz Herbal has shot into international limelight for their miraculous results. The ever-changing ideas in beauty science have been handpicked by Shahnaz Herbal, based on specialised skin and hair care expertise. They believe in a high level of quality too, because apart from other things, they have a name to reckon with. Today, Shahnaz Herbal has become a hallmark in safety and protection...a name they would protect at all costs. Shahnaz Herbal is a beautiful way of life, waiting for you to discover it...

Plant Products for Beauty

PLANT products have a long history of therapeutic use. Not only are they a powerful store-house of valuable minerals and vitamins, but have definite cura-tive properties. Some of them are extremely versatile and have more than one action. They possess a strength that we need to know and understand, since natural therapy which is guided by knowledge is the only answer to many of our ills. They also protect us from the after-effects of synthetic remedies and help to restore the natural balances. These are some of their unique benefits. It is no wonder that plant products are ideal ingre-dients for cosmetics.

Carrots: They are rich sources of Vitamin A, the factor that is vital for the health of the skin. They form important ingredients in nourishing creams and face masks.

Camomile: It possesses healing properties and is a versatile cosmetic aid. It is used to control acne, soothe skin irrita-tions and cleanse the skin of im-purities.

Comfrey: Its oil has medicinal properties, which benefits dehy-drated skins.

Cinnamon: Its oil extracts are used for massage. It soothes sun damaged skins. The oil is also good for teeth.

Cloves: They have powerful antiseptic qualities and have a freshening effect. They heal and soothe eruptions and rashy condi-tions. They have been used in medicated creams and packs. They also benefit the teeth and freshen the breath.

Eucalyptus: Also has antiseptic qualities. Soothes, heals and refreshes the skin. Ideal ingredient for skin problems associated with oily skins.

Lavender: It is one of the most versatile cosmetic aids. It has several actions on the skin, apart from its soft and sweet natural aroma. It refreshes and tones the skin and forms an ingredient in body shampoos and cleansers.

Mint: This has a cooling effect, apart from a healing action. It is known to clear blemishes. Used in skin tonics to tone and refresh oily skins.

Fennel: Soothes inflammations and is good for deep-pore cleansing. It has also been used in herbal hair rinses.

Rose: It has been in use since the ancient times. Rose petals are used to make rose water, which is an ideal base for skin tonics. It softens coarse skin and porcelains the pores. It has been incorporated in lotions, creams and packs for its soothing, gentle action. It has a luxurious aroma.

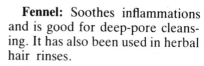

Sage: Its healing powers are well known. It was used during ancient times to cure many disorders. Has been used in herbal hair tonics and shampoos to stimulate the scalp. It is said to have hair darkening properties too.

Thyme: It is a well known antiseptic ingredient and was used to disinfect and heal injuries. It has an astringent effect on the skin and also tones it. It has versatile uses and forms an ingredient for skin tonics, hair tonics and shampoos.

Sandalwood: It has a powerful antiseptic and germicidal effect. Has been incorporated into protective creams for all skin types. It soothes rashy conditions and heals the skin. It is an important ingredient of 'sunscreen' creams. Heals and protects at the same time. It has a natural haunting aroma.

Geranium: It has powerful antiseptic properties.

Lemongrass: It contains Vitamin A. Also clears skin blemishes and refreshes the skin. It has a natural fresh aroma.

Wheatgerm: It contains Vitamin E and is an anti-wrinkle ingredient. It soothes, heals and irons out lines. Has been used in nourishing cream.

Lemon: It is a wonderful natural cleanser. It cleanses without disturbing the natural acid mantle of the skin. It is also a natural astringent and helps to tighten the skin. It is very refreshing. Lemon is most versatile and has been included in face creams, pre-bath creams, cleansers and masks.

Ginseng: Another versatile natural ingredient is ginseng. It has a powerful cleansing action and is good for deep-pore cleansing and to restore the acid alkaline balance of the skin.

Almond: It is one of the best known cosmetic aids. There is a long record of its use. It smoothens the skin and has a skin tightening effect, with a very gentle action. At the same time, it refines and moisturises the skin. It is an ideal ingredient for face creams, especially for the skin around the eyes. It has a mild bleaching effect and removes under-eye circles.

Apricot: It contains Vitamin A and has a rejuvenating effect on the skin. It contains polyunsaturated fats and is good for skin creams. Smooths away wrinkles and lightens stretch marks. It has been used in body and hand creams and is also an important ingredient of face packs.

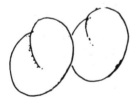

Beauty from the Kitchen Shelf

EGGS: Give yourself an egg face lift. Beat a raw egg and apply it as a mask on the face and neck. Lie down and relax for twenty minutes and then rinse off with water. Eggs help to tighten the pores and nourish the skin. They can give you a quick 'face lift' after a tiring day. The white of an egg is a wonderful cleanser. Apply it on the head half-an-hour before your shampoo. For a special conditioning effect, beat an egg and two teaspoonfuls of brandy. Apply it before washing the hair.

Tea: Soak cotton wool pads in cold tea and use them as eye pads to brighten tired eyes. Keep used tea leaves. Boil them in enough water and use the 'tea water' as a last rinse after your shampoo. It helps to add shine to the hair.

Salt: Bathing the eyes in warm water, to which a little salt has been added, can really brighten them up. It helps to relieve puffiness too. Alternatively, dip cotton wool pads in salt water solution of one tablespoon salt and a pint of warm water. Use them as eye pads. Soaking the feet in warm water with about three tablespoons of salt helps to relieve fatigue.

Castor Oil: It is certainly more pleasant when used externally! Rub it into the scalp at bedtime and wash your hair next morning. Castor oil is unsaturated and is said to rejuvenate the hair. Try another method—rub castor oil into the scalp. Dip a large towel in hot water, wring it out and tie it around the head for a while. This allows greater penetration of oil deep into the surface of the scalp. Castor oil may also be applied on eyelashes to darken and thicken them.

Honey: One of the best natural moisturisers is honey. It can be applied by itself on the skin to give it a soft, moist, satiny look. For oily skins, mix stiffly beaten egg white with honey. For dry skins, add a little cream of milk. A spoonful of honey in your bath water is said to relieve fatigue and induce sleep.

Cucumber: Cucumber juice or slices as eye pads are common home remedies. Cucumber has a cleansing, soothing and mild astringent effect on the skin. Grated cucumber with a little milk can be applied on the face for a refreshing skin toning effect. Wiping the skin with cucumber slices can benefit oily skins. After a hot day out in the sun, a cucumber treatment can be most soothing.

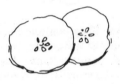

Potato: They help to clear skin blemishes. In fact, potatoes are said to benefit conditions of eczema. Grate potatoes and extract the juice. Apply on the skin. Potato slices can also be used to wipe the skin. They have a tightening effect and help to reduce puffiness around the eyes. Use the slices as eye pads or grate raw potato and make eye pads.

Cabbage: They contain valuable minerals, like other vegetables. Boil cabbage in a little water. Cool the water and use it to wash the face. It is a skin nourishing treatment.

Orange: Collect orange peels and dry them in the sun. Grind and add to facial mask mixtures. They are extremely good for toning the skin.

Papaya: They contain enzymes, which help to soften the dead skin cells and remove them. Use the pulp as a face mask. It is good for all skin types.

Carrot: They help to soothe dry, sensitive skins. Boil them in a little water, then cool and mash into a pulp. Use it as a mask.

Yoghurt: It has several benefits. It contains enzymes and is a wonderful natural cleanser. It also helps to maintain the good health of the skin and scalp. Apply it on the face after a wash. Rinse off after twenty minutes with luke warm water. It is especially good for oily, spotty skins. It can also be applied on the scalp before the shampoo. It cleanses the scalp and adds body to the hair.

Before helping yourself to the goodies on your kitchen shelf, remember to follow the basic principles of hygiene while chopping and grating ingredients. Also that beauty is a matter of regularity and patience.

SKIN CARE

The Structure of the Skin

THE skin is one of the most intriguing organs of the body. It performs many important functions and is highly efficient. It is essentially a covering, but does much more than merely hold us together. The unbroken skin is impervious to air, water, dust and bacteria and protects us from all these. It also eliminates waste matter and regulates and maintains body temperature. It reflects the state of our internal health and our emotions so faithfully. Depending on the part it covers and the function it is expected to perform, the thickness and sensitivity of the skin varies. The skin of the scalp, palm and sole is thick, while the skin on the face, lips and genital organs is thin, sensitive and mobile. This living, breathing organ is extremely tough and yet, so soft, resilient and flexible.

Broadly speaking, the skin has two layers—the epidermis, which is the most superficial layer and the dermis or inner layer. Distributed between these two layers is a complex system of nerves, blood vessels, oil glands, sweat glands, hair follicles, sensory cells and sensory nerve endings. Sensations of heat, cold, pressure and pain are promptly conveyed by the skin's system of nerves.

The epidermis or top layer is made up of several rows of living cells, covered with a horny layer of dead cells. These are constantly being shed and replaced by cells from the deeper layers. The epidermis protects the inner layer.

Beneath the epidermis is the dermis or 'true skin', as it is also called. It is in the dermis that living tissue exists. The dermal layer is supplied with nutrients from the blood stream. The dermis contains supporting tissue, which gives the skin its tone and resilience. It also contains the sweat and oil glands. The surface ends of the oil glands form the pores of the skin. They secrete sebum, an oily, slightly acid film, which is deposited on the surface of the skin. This helps to lubricate the skin, while its acid content resists bacterial attacks and keeps the skin in a healthy condition. The sweat glands help to eliminate wastes and regulate body temperature.

A network of capillary blood vessels supply oxygen and nutrients to the skin and lymphatic vessels drain away waste products. Hair is found almost all over the body, with variations in length and texture in different areas. The hair root lies beneath the skin.

In the basal layer of the epidermis are cells which produce a pigment called melanin. This determines the colour of the skin. Melanin protects the skin from the sun's rays by acting as a natural sunscreen. The amount of pigment in the skin increases when there is exposure to sunlight. This is a protective response and helps to shield the inner layer.

Nature has designed the skin to maintain itself. However, internal and external factors do affect its health, giving rise to imbalances. When the oil glands are over-active, the skin may be greasy. When they are under-active, the result will be a dry skin. Or, there may be a lack of moisture. That is why we should understand our skin type and rectify the imbalances, if any.

Skin Types

IT is essential to know about the 'look' and 'feel' of your skin to know what type of skin you have. Skin types fall into four major categories: normal, oily, dry and combination.

Normal skin: This skin type is neither oily nor dry. It has a soft, velvety texture. Colour glows under its translucent surface. Beautiful as it is, it needs care, if it is to last.

People with normal skins start showing signs of age and wrinkling sooner than others, if they tend to neglect their skins. Daily cleansing, toning and nourishing is the adequate care for normal skin.

Oily skin: In this kind of skin, the sebaceous (oil-producing) glands are overactive. They produce more oil than is needed, which oozes up, giving the skin a greasy shine. The pores are enlarged and the skin has a coarse look. It is also prone to blackheads, pimples and acne.

Oily skin need special cleansing to keep the pores unclogged. The flow of sebum (oil) increases during adolescence and starts decreasing with age. At other times of life, like pregnancy and meno-pause, hormonal imbalances can also upset the oil balance and increase sebaceous gland activity.

Dry skin: If you have a dry skin, you fall in the category of the majority. Your skin lacks both sebum and moisture. It looks fine-textured, transparent, patchy and fragile. There may be tiny expression lines and there may even be crêpeness. It flakes and chaps easily.

There are many factors which affect dry skins and make them even more dry. For instance, washing with soap and water not only removes grime but also the natural oils that protect the skin. Exposure to the sun, air-conditioners and heaters also take their toll.

Dry skins need attention by way of products which supply emollients and moisture. The emollient provides the oils, keeps the skin lubricated and traps moisture in the skin. A moisturiser increases the water content of the outer layers of the skin, giving it a soft, moist look.

Many women find that they have to wage a constant war against their dry skins in order to prevent premature ageing.

Combination skin: This type of skin has a greasy area, while the rest is dry or normal. The forehead, nose and chin, i.e. the T-zone, may be greasy and the rest dry.

Combination skins are very common and are one of the most frequently misunderstood and mistreated skins. This type of skin requires separate treatment for each area. However, both the dry and greasy areas need moisturising.

Remember that oil is not moisture. Pay special attention to cleansing and use a skin tonic to tone up the skin. Like oily skins, the oily panel may be prone to unappealing clusters of blackheads and enlarged pores.

Apart from these major skin types, there may be other types which are exaggerated versions of the major skin types, like dehydrated skins, sensitive skins, acne-blemished skins, ageing skins or hydrated skins.

Sensitive skins react to external and internal changes and sometimes show a flushed or reddened look or may itch.

Ageing skins are 'time tired' skins. They are the result of passing days, with clusters of wrinkles and tiny criss-cross lines. The skin around the throat begins to sag.

Hydrated skins have too much moisture and look puffy and congested. They suffer from poor circulation which causes congestion and a swollen, puffy look. This condition indicates that the skin may have become clogged with toxins and waste matter. It is usually found in older people.

The first step to skin care is to identify your type of skin and then follow the prescribed medication and methods to care for it.

If you want a good skin, the most important thing is to take care of it daily. It should be a matter of habit, like brushing your teeth. Your diet also plays an important part, so does getting adequate sleep and exercise.

In fact, if you would like your skin story to have an happy ending, follow these basic rules:

1. Cleanse your skin twice a day with products suited to the particular type.
2. See a beauty therapist regularly after the age of 25.
3. Learn to treat the skin according to its type.
4. Avoid the sun.
5. Avoid smoking.
6. Drink eight glasses of water daily.
7. Use a face mask once a week.
8. Exercise regularly.
9. Remember that regular care and routine pay rich dividends.
10. Neglect accelerates ageing more than anything else.

Daily Care for Dry Skin   *SHADEW, SHABASE SHAMOIST, SHACLEANSE SHALIFE*

THE invigorating winter season can, besides giving you rosy cheeks, absorb all the moisture away, leaving you with a taut, dry skin. The signs of a dry skin are:

1. Your skin has a few flaky patches that disappear with rich moisturising creams.

2. Your skin looks fine textured, which means that the pores are not visible.

3. You have tiny expression lines around the eyes. These do not disappear, but seem to have come to stay.

4. The skin of the neck and cheeks looks crepey.

The human skin is structured to breathe in oxygen. In order to do so, it should be absolutely clean. There is also, a very high moisture content in the cells of the skin. This water content decreases slowly with age due to hormonal or vitamin deficiencies. The moisture glands of the skin get more ineffective, resulting in a dry and prematurely wrinkled skin. In fact, water is even more important to a dry skin than oil.

Excessive dry skins should be treated with those preparations, which are designed to supply moisture to the skin.

Apart from a good healthy diet, an eight-hour sleep schedule and lots of fresh fruit and vegetables, exercise in fresh air and a daily beauty routine, are essential, if you would like to prevent your skin from drying up.

First on your routine, should be cleansing. Most women use some kind of make-up on their skin, so cleansing is very essential. You need a cleanser, which will remove all pore-clogging debris effectively, without leaving the skin taut and dry or stripped of its natural protective mantle. A cactus cleanser, with a lemon base, is best.

Cactus has one of the highest moisture retention capacities and is ideal for rehydrating the skin. The cleanser must be massaged gently, into the skin with a light upward and outward stroke, paying particular attention to the creases of the nose under the chin, neck and ear lobes.

Always use moist cotton wool to prevent it from absorbing moisture from the skin. This routine should be followed in the morning and at bedtime. Lemon is not only a natural cleanser but a natural bleach and after a period of time, the skin begins to look fairer, while the cactus would stagger the onslaught of the wrinkling and lining process.

The second step in your daily routine should be toning, which is an essential follow-up of the cleansing process. Toning removes the last stages of cleanser and dissolves dirt. It stimulates surface circulation. It is advisable to use a skin tonic lotion.

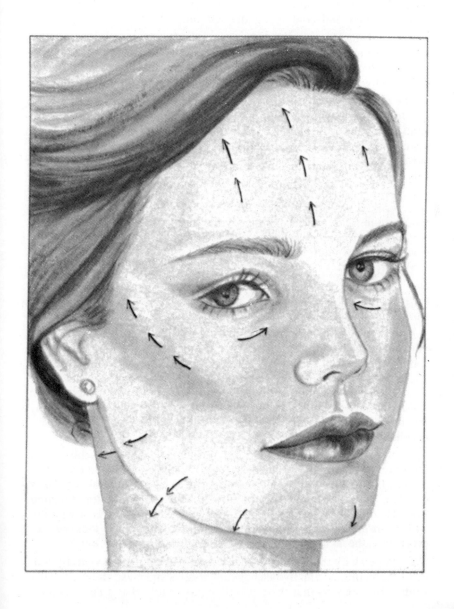

Pour half a bottle of skin tonic in a dish, and soak in it a few small pads of cotton wool and leave it in the fridge. Thus it will always be ready, soaked and cold to be dabbed onto the face.

Before throwing away the pad, press and roll it in an upward direction on the face and neck. A skin tonic, with a mint and honey base, would be excellent for delicate and parched skin. Skin tonic braces the skin and tightens the pores, especially under the eyes and on the jawline.

The next step is nourishing the skin, which is essential, if you would like to prevent dryness. When you are asleep the skin is busy replacing dead skin cells with new ones. Sleeping is a very important time for beauty, because there is no sun, wind or dust to bother the skin. The dermal tissues can relax and be nourished and replenished without external disturbances.

Every night, a nourishing cream with preferably an orange base, must be smoothed upwards over the face and from the chin downwards, to relax taut muscles and accelerate circulation. If you feel that your skin is very dry, use a second application. A nourishing cream, with Vitamin E, would work wonders.

The area which needs special care is the area around the eyes. This area lacks sebaceous glands, which supply oil to the skin. Hence, the area around the eyes can suffer most from dryness, as the skin there would line, wrinkle and darken first.

Apply an almond-lanolin cream from the inner corner of the eyes outwards, very gently. Be careful to remove the cream with moist cotton wool before bedtime, as keeping it on while asleep may cause swollen and puffy lids. This is because, the sensitive eye area should not be covered with cream for eight hours. Almond being a natural bleach, will also help to lighten the dark circles around the eyes. The lanolin will supply the much needed oils to this area. An almond-lanolin cream is also excellent for dry, dark lips.

Lastly, keep in mind that soap and purifying elements like chlorine in the water have a drying effect on the skin. What is therefore essential, is a special pre-bath cream, which contains turmeric and special moisturisers. This should be applied on the face, before a bath or before washing the face, in order to ward off the drying and harmful effects of washing with soap and water. A gentle vanishing cream goes a long way in protecting the skin from getting dehydrated during the day.

Equipped with this knowledge, you should be able to prevent the skin from becoming a victim to the changing seasons and make the most of the winter. Remember, that there is nothing as beautiful as a flawless skin.

Moisture—The Skin's Basic Need

THE skin's main requirement is moisture, which helps to soften the outer layer and keep it in a youthful condition. Moisture has to be supplied to the skin in the form of an emulsion of oil and water, to which other ingredients can be added.

What is a moisturiser? A good moisturiser should perform a few basic functions. It should supply moisture to the skin. It should be a 'humectant', so that it attracts moisture to the skin from the atmosphere. It should also form a barrier between the skin and the elements, so that the rate of evaporation of moisture from the skin slows down. Yet, it should be porous, so that the skin can 'breathe'. Moisturisers should therefore help to achieve a perfect balance of oil and moisture, so that the skin is kept soft and smooth.

When the skin degenerates due to age, exposure to the elements and other causes, it stops producing enough natural oil. Consequently, it also loses its ability to hold moisture. The results which are apparent on the skin surface are wrinkles, loss of elasticity and a dry, rough texture. In fact, these effects can cause the skin to age prematurely.

Since the skin is constantly exposed to external factors, the loss of moisture takes place all the time. This loss has to be replaced. Exposure to the sun is known to cause excessive damage in terms of dehydration of the skin. Artificial heating and cooling devices also rob the skin of its natural moisture. Even the water that you use to wash your face can cause dryness, when it has been treated with chemicals to purify it. Outdoor activities and sport, like swimming, can cause excessive moisture depletion.

Supplying moisture to the skin by the use of suitable cosmetic-aids is the only way to prevent the skin from drying up. This should form an integral part of the daily skin-care routine. It is also important to choose your products with care. We are fortunate that research with various ingredients has made such advanced cosmetic-aids available to us.

Moisturisers are not only available in cream or liquid form, but moisturising masks have also been devised to increase the skin's capacity to retain moisture, or to replenish moisture depletion. Let us take a look at the methods that can be employed to moisturise the skin, prevent moisture loss and improve the skin's moisture retention ability.

Nourishing the Skin with Herbs

NOURISHING is probably one of the most common phrases in beauty terminology. The dictionary defines the word 'nourish' as 'sustain with food; cherish; nurse'. Just as the body must be nourished with appropriate food elements, the skin also requires sustenance and must be 'fed'. It is no wonder, therefore, that the word 'nourishment' is so appropriately used in beauty care.

To most of us, nourishing means the application of cream and the ritual is performed by many as part of their night-care routine. However, beauty techniques today lay a great deal of emphasis, not only on methods, but also on the nature of the product that is used. The individual characteristics of the skin determines the best way of providing nourishment. Basically, nourishing creams are products that lubricate the skin, keep it soft and help it to retain its natural moisture. It is the combination of oil and moisture that keeps the skin soft, smooth and supple. As their task is to lubricate, nourishing creams are thicker and richer than moisturising creams. They are needed by skin types that lack natural oil. Mature skins, in which oil gland activity has slackened, also need daily lubrication. From this, it is apparent that oily skins, which produce excess oils, cannot be 'fed' with rich nourishing creams. They would require a different 'diet'!

The best way to apply nourishing creams is to first cleanse the skin thoroughly with a rehydrant cleanser. Then the cream is massaged into the skin. This helps it to absorb the product better. Normally, the skin absorbs all it can in about twenty minutes. Keeping the cream on much beyond this time, does not benefit it in any way. In fact it may just attract dirt or clog the pores. Once the skin has absorbed the cream, it should be removed with moist cotton wool to prevent moisture loss. The cream should not be left on overnight.

The ingredients of skin-care aids have evoked great interest in recent years. Not only have better products been devised, but the effort has been made to eliminate harmful substances. It has been seen that chemical substances penetrate into the inner layer of the skin and cause irritative reactions. Herbal ingredients, on the other hand, contain properties that are extremely beneficial to the skin and also eliminate harmful effects. Herbs also have therapeutic value, which make them a highly appropriate means of maintaining beauty and restoring beauty to the skin.

Among natural products that can nourish the skin, there are those that we come across daily, as well as others that were once part of our ancient therapies, with exotic names and remarkable values. Almond extracts are commonly used in both creams and masks in combination with appropriate bases and other ingredients. Almond, with a lanolin base, is ideal for nourishing the region around the eyes. Almond meal is added to basic mask powders. Like almond, apricot is also nourishing for the skin. It contains Vitamin A, which keeps the skin soft and free of wrinkles. Various natural ingredients contain Vitamin E, which heals scar tissue, eases out lines and restores elasticity to the skin. Vitamin E oil, by itself, is thick and sticky, whereas plant products that contain Vitamin E, make the skin-care routine easier and more pleasant. Natural products have their own delicate fragrances too.

A good nourishing cream, therefore, can be called a 'skin-food' cream, providing nourishment and improving the skin's functions, so that it can attain maximum good health and beauty. A skin-food cream, containing cabbage extract, carrot, wheat germ, has been found ideal for skin nourishment. Carrot and wheat germ are both rich in Vitamin E. Carrot also contains Vitamin A, while cabbage contains valuable minerals that have a rejuvenating effect and prevent skin blemishes.

Natural ingredients like honey, milk, yoghurt and egg are valuable beauty aids, as they are nourishing for the skin. Eggs, for instance, contain lecithin, which is extremely nourishing, as it contains protein and phosphorous. Thus, natural products help to provide the skin with the elements that are required.

The number of herbs that are being used in beauty treatments are so many and so varied. Some have been used since ancient times—like extracts of rose, jasmine and lavender. These extracts, like many others, have stood the test of time. They are ideal for oily and problem skins and help to improve their texture and health. Similarly, herbs like comfrey, camomile, sesame, when added to nourishing creams and lotions, help to improve skin colour and texture. Comfrey is particularly suited to sensitive skins and cures irritations. Camomile is an emollient plant. Camomile oil is added to nourishing creams, as it helps to soften rough, coarse skin.

Since the skin absorbs products applied on it, masks should be used to nourish the skin. They not only complete the cleansing procedure, but stimulate the skin, improve blood circulation and improve the skin's capacity to absorb the product.

Skin nourishment, therefore, has wider connotations. It just does not mean lubrication. That is just one aspect of it. A balance between oil and moisture must be maintained. The care of the skin must be such that, it improves the health of the skin as a whole, by helping it to perform its various functions efficiently. A healthy skin is one which has a smooth texture, an even colour tone and feels soft to the touch. Through proper nourishment, the texture, colour, blood circulation and the skin's ability to absorb products improve. A wide array of beauty aids are available especially when we choose them from nature. The way nature has provided us with the means to sustain our bodies, she has gifted us with products to care for its external beauty. Why not spare a thought for the skin and ask, "Has my skin eaten today?"

Cleansing of Oily Skin

SHAZEMA, SHAMINT
SHABASE, SHASILK
SHAROSE

PERHAPS the most important part in the daily care of oily skins is cleansing.

A proper method of cleansing is the best form of preventive care that can be given to keep the skin free of blackheads, spots and other blemishes.

An oily skin, as the name implies, is one in which the sebaceous or oil-producing glands are over active. The excess oil causes the pores to become enlarged giving the skin a thick, coarse look.

As surface grease tends to attract dirt, an oily skin acquires a dirty surface film, that needs to be removed daily. If this is not done, various problems associated with oily skins set in.

By considering the characteristics of a greasy skin, we can adopt a proper cleansing procedure. Due to the excess secretion of oil, skin always looks shiny and toneless. The enlarged pores give it a thick texture and make the skin prone to blackhead formations, leading to pimples and acne.

Blackheads are formed when oil collects and hardens in the pores of the skin. Not only does oily skin attract more dirt, but dead cells are continuously being shed by it. Dirt, oil, sweat wastes, stale make-up and decomposed cells tend to clog and block the pores, giving the skin a dirty appearance.

What makes daily cleansing even more important is that, in many cases, the oil glands are further stimulated to excrete oil. This can happen when harsh cleansing methods are followed or when the skin is subjected to excessive steam or heat.

Even a diet containing excessive fats, carbohydrates and sugar can cause increased secretion of oil. The daily cleansing method helps to lift the dirt and waste matter, decrease surface grease and help the skin to function better. This, in turn, would help the skin to look fresh and stay healthy

When we adopt a cleansing procedure, we should keep a few basic aspects in mind. First, the surface film of oil and dirt must be removed. Secondly, the pores must be free of accumulated grease, so that blackheads are discouraged. Thirdly, the texture of the skin should improve.

All this should be achieved without creating an alkaline environment on the skin as this would leave the skin predisposed to bacterial attacks. A healthy skin is slightly acidic. This natural acid mantle must be protected or restored.

This aspect is particularly important, as most cleansing methods can upset the normal acid-alkaline balance of the skin. In their efforts to remove surface oil, people with greasy skins wash their face too often with harsh alkaline soaps, destroying the natural acid mantle.

When it comes to choosing products for cleansing, thick creams and gels are taboo. These cosmetics would actually cause pore-clogging. Even liquid cleansers are not really effective, especially when the skin is prone to blackheads. The products that are used are therefore as important as the methods that are followed. The ideal cleansing routine is one that includes two separate procedures.

First the skin should be washed with a medicated soap, using lukewarm water. This helps remove surface oil and dirt. Special non-alkaline soaps in cream form, are available and have been used with success even on skins affected by acne. These non-oily products contain herbal ingredients that actually restore the acid mantle.

The skin should be rinsed with water. Once the skin is cleansed of surface grease a pore-cleansing method should be followed. This is based on a gentle derm-abrasive action which cleanses the skin of dead cells and dislodges hardened oil from the pores.

A mixture of beauty grains and skin tonic is rubbed gently on to the skin. It is left to dry and then rinsed off. This procedure has helped even in cases of stubborn blackheads, which are either removed or loosened. Daily cleansing, in this manner, also helps to discourage blackheads being formed.

A circular motion should be used to rub the grains gently, concentrating on the nose and chin areas. This stimulates the skin, removes dead cells and unclogs the pores. The skin tonic has a rose base which has a healing action and also helps to tighten the pores and refresh the skin.

Gradually with time, the pores shrink, the texture improves and the skin acquires a smooth, translucent look. It also improves circulation, giving the skin a healthy glow.

Whatever the skin type, it is bound to benefit from an appropriate cleansing routine. It is only through proper cleansing that problems like acne can be avoided. Deep pore cleansing helps in improving both the texture and colour of the skin, apart from correcting the imbalances.

Taking proper care of the skin is basically a matter of awareness of the right and wrong procedures that one can adopt. In fact, it is better not to cleanse the skin at all, rather than employ the wrong methods. Both neglect and abuse spell death to skin beauty, and the choice depends on you!

Care for Combination Skins

THE care of a combination skin does present a problem, as it seems to have the worst features of both dry and oily skin. The effort should be towards striking a balance, to reduce the oiliness of the greasy parts and lubricate the dry areas. One should use two skin care routines and treat the different areas as two individual skins. This may sound very difficult, but once you understand the characteristics and choose the right cosmetics, the daily routine should be quite simple.

Cleansing comes first. The dry areas should be wiped with a light rehydrant gel, using moist cotton wool. Apply a medicated soap on the oily areas and rinse off with water. Rub a mixture of beauty grains and skin tonic on areas that are prone to blackheads. Wash off. Tone the entire face with skin tonic, using a cotton wool pad. Pat the skin briskly. This cleansing routine should be followed in the morning and before bedtime.

The night.care routine should include a light massage with a nourishing cream on the dry regions. Choose a product that is not too oily. Cleanse and massage the neck too. Wipe off all the cream with moist cotton wool after twenty minutes. Apply an almond under-eye cream around the eyes and wipe off with moist cotton wool after ten minutes. If there are any spots or pimples on the oily areas, apply an anti-pimple lotion only on the eruptions and leave it on. In case there are scars left by acne, rub an anti-blemish ointment it into the scars and leave it on all night.

A few cosmetic-aids, common to both types, are also required. A suitable sunscreen would protect the skin from dehydration, and environmental pollutants. Whenever the skin feels dry, use a light liquid moisturiser. A skin tonic with rose base is a very versatile product. It helps to tone and refresh the skin and acts as a quick pick-me-up during the day. The skin care routine without a face mask is incomplete. Choose one according to the need. If there is acne or pimples, a medicated mask is the best answer.

The Blackhead Menace

BLACKHEADS are so common, yet many people do not know what they are. They know even less about dealing with them.

It is a condition that cannot be cured because it is a manifestation of a particular tendency based on the type of skin. In other words, the primary cause of blackheads cannot be eliminated. However, they can be controlled and even prevented by taking regular care of the skin.

Blackheads are caused by over active sebaceous glands—the oil-producing glands of the skin. The excess secretion of oil expands and thickens the pores of the skin. The oil collects in the pores and hardens into a plug. The pores are then clogged with hardened sebum or oil. Since the pores are open, the tip of the clogged grease is exposed to the air and oxidises, turning black. Hence, the name blackheads.

Oily skins, naturally tend to attract dirt and grime from the environment and these pollutants also collect in the pores with the hardened oil. Blackheads cause the pores to be further enlarged and people with oily skins end up with a skin texture that is coarse and rough.

The counterpart of the blackhead is the whitehead, which is also caused by the collection of sebum in the pores, but in this case the pores are not open and the sebum is not exposed to the air

Apart from the fact that blackheads look unsightly, they are the cause of acne. The primary acne lesion is, in fact, a blackhead. When a pore is fully blocked, the oil gland can get infected resulting in a pimple. If the infection progresses, it ruptures the well of the oil glands and attacks the inner layer of the skin, giving way to an acne condition. In acne infections, the inner layer is destroyed and this is the cause of intensive scarring.

Therefore, it is obvious that the control of blackheads is one way of preventing acne. Blackheads not only appear on the face, but on the back, chest and other areas that are rich in sebaceous glands.

The vital part of the treatment is proper cleansing. Soap and water washing is not enough to keep the pores free of hardened oil. However, washing the face twice a day with a medicated soap and lukewarm water helps reduce the oiliness of the skin surface and eliminate the chances of infections.

Washing the face with soap more than twice a day is not recommended, as the acid mantle of the skin has to be protected to avoid bacterial infections. The skin can be rinsed with plain water often, to keep it free of environmental pollutants.

Washing must be followed by a more thorough cleansing to dislodge hardened sebum and keep the pores clean. This is done by using a cleanser, like beauty grains mixed with a rose-based skin tonic. The mixture is rubbed gently on the skin, left on to dry for a few minutes and then washed off.

This method of cleansing is highly effective for the removal of blackheads and also for their prevention. It also helps to smoothen the skin and improve its texture. The skin tonic is used to reduce oiliness, close the pores and beautify the skin. Thus the pores of the skin are gradually 'porcelained' over a period of time and the entire look and feel of the skin improves.

After washing, the skin needs to be protected from environmental pollutants, more so if you are going out. This can be done by using a cream containing sandalwood which forms an invisible protective film on the skin. Sandalwood has germicidal qualities. The surface oil is controlled, and the skin is kept moistured. In other words, it brings about a better balance between the oil and moisture contents of the skin.

A daily mask is another way of preventing and controlling blackheads. Masks help to deep-cleanse the skin. In fact, they can be powerful cleansers to keep the pores free of grease. This itself helps to porcelain the pores, as sebum is not allowed to get collected and enlarge them. To be effective, the mask must be applied daily.

A specialised mask has been used in the treatment of the most persistent blackheads, with extremely satisfactory results. It consists of a herbal powder which is mixed with a seaweed lotion, honey, yoghurt and the white of an egg. This is applied, left on to dry and removed by dampening the skin with water and using gentle circulatory strokes. Finally, the skin is washed with plenty of water. The skin's texture improves, the pores shrink and blackheads are prevented from forming. This also helps keep the skin smooth and youthful, as it removes the accumulation of dead skin cells. The extraction of blackheads also becomes much easier after the application of the mask.

Blackhead extraction is a professional job and it should be left to people who know exactly how to do it. I would like to emphasise on this aspect particularly. Never pick at them or try to remove them yourself. Tampering with the skin by forcing blackheads out brutally can damage skin tissue by destroying the inner layer. Perfect hygiene must also be maintained.

I enforce a strict clinical practice of sterilisation of blackhead extractors or comedones, and keep them dipped in an antiseptic solution. Neglect of simple hygienic procedure in beauty parlours can lead to infectious conditions.

Steaming the face is a common procedure and does help to dislodge blackheads. However, I do not advocate steaming, as it enlarges the pores further and does nothing to improve the skin texture. It also activates the oil glands to secrete more sebum. Unless adequate methods are used to reduce surface oiliness and close the pores, the problem of prevention cannot be tackled.

The sebispir is one of the latest gadgets used for the removal of blackheads. It works on a suction principle and helps to bring the blackheads to the surface, after which they can be easily extracted. Skin damage and chances of infection are very effectively eliminated. The extraction must be followed by procedures to close the pores. Application of germicidal products protects the skin. Whiteheads should never be removed with blackhead extractors. The preventive treatment for whiteheads is the same, since the primary cause is the same.

All said and done, what should be apparent is that daily care is the only way to avoid most skin blemishes. One must know the characteristics of one's own skin in order to pinpoint the cause of simple problems. Skin care has become so advanced and highly specialised. Professional guidance is within the reach of everyone, and so are the appropriate products. Modern techniques in cosmetic chemistry have been geared towards providing products in a form that requires minimum time and effort. The woman of today has no reason to subject her skin to neglect and abuse—the two factors that are responsible for most skin problems.

ACNE: Prevention and Treatment
SHADERM
SHACLOVE
SHACLEAR

THE enormous facial disfigurement left in the wake of acne is due to the fact that many people do not know that acne is a curable disorder. Many regard acne as an inevitable part of growing up and wait to grow out of it—until it results in psychological and physical scarring just at a time when one wants to look one's best. The best way to define acne would be to say that acne "is the sum total of the consequences of over-activity and disorderly activity of the sebaceous glands."

These glands, being more numerous on the face, give rise to eruptions and disturbances when they are over-active, causing the condition that we call acne. With the over secretion of oil in the sebaceous duct, the excess oil enters the oil sac, which expands in order to retain the oil. When the pores cannot hold any more, the excess oil oozes out, enlarging the pores in the process.

The first result is blackheads. When the sebaceous secretion thickens, the pores of the glands become clogged with the oil, hardening into a solid plug. When the tip is exposed to the air, it oxidises and turns dark. This is a blackhead and not dirt, as many people commonly believe.

The blackhead can be removed, but this does not help the oil gland to stop its activity. This is where professional treatment becomes necessary. Neglected blackheads irritate the surrounding tissues of the skin, resulting in inflammation, setting the stage for pimples and acne.

Acne conditions include whiteheads, blackheads, pustules and cysts. Sometimes there is a total flare-up of the condition into a violent form, as in acne vulgaris. There are various stages of infection. If it is not controlled, it can even lead to a septic skin. Skin problems, associated with acne, are extremely tenacious. That is why it should be controlled in good time, before it becomes a chronic condition.

I advise my clients to have blood, urine and stool tests. Very often these tests reveal the existence of worms or some intestinal infection. Even if these infections are mild, they should be treated with the necessary medication and diet control. It is also necessary to carry out follow up tests to ascertain that the complaint has been removed. If it is not, then further medication will be necessary. If the tests are clear, vitamin supplements, a low-fat diet, salads and fresh fruits will help to keep things under control. Simple exercise like jogging helps to accelerate blood circulation in a sluggish system.

From my experience of treating acne cases, I have found that the treatment should be manifold and geared towards the following:

Appropriate cleansing.
Discouraging and dislodging blackheads.
Reducing/controlling oiliness of the skin.
Closing the pores.
Curing the existing eruptions:
Preventing further infection.

Discouraging wrinkling (common in acute acne).
Providing a protection against environmental pollution.
Providing a suitable medicated base to moisturise the skin and conceal the conditions.
Removal of scars.

The first step to treating acne is appropriate cleansing not just to keep the skin free of dirt, but to keep it free of oil—the aim being to keep the skin as dry as possible. This can be achieved by washing the face with a medicated soap at least twice a day. Large pores and a dull, sallow complexion are characteristics of oily skins. If blackheads are removed properly and in good time, acne can be prevented. The best way is to have them removed by a beauty therapist and then apply a prescribed medication.

A word of warning: never pick pimples or squeeze blackheads yourself. You will only damage skin tissue and cause the infection to spread. It is also important to avoid oily face creams, cleansing creams or any greasy preparations, which are all pore-clogging cosmetics.

Very often, acne victims experience a superficial dryness of the skin, which is not always understood. This dryness is not due to lack of oil but because of lack of moisture in the outer layers of the skin caused by washing with chlorinated water or the use of drying agents, which are common in acne treatments. Such people go to beauty parlours and are given facial massages to counteract the dryness and then find that the acne condition has flared up. This happens as a result of massage with oily creams, which actually provokes the activity of the oil glands.

I have had clients coming to me with an acne flare-up after being given a facial massage, when what they should have actually been prescribed was an appropriate moisturiser made from flower extracts, cucumber, or honey to get relief from dryness.

Foundations should also be avoided. Many young people inquire about the use of make up as an aspect of concealment. The use of normal foundations starts a vicious circle—the more one tries to hide the blemishes, the more blemishes there are to hide!

To my mind, a cure can best be achieved by the use of a herbal facial conditioner, combined with honey, yoghurt and egg white. Honey is a natural moisturiser, yoghurt is lactic acid and a natural whitener, while egg white has tissue-building and skin-tightening properties. These three natural products combined with the herbal powder and applied once a day can achieve two important purposes. It dermabrases the skin, ironing out lines, wrinkles, acne scars, spots and even smallpox scars, and also gets rid of dead epithelial cells. In the process, the skin becomes clear.

The herbal powder mixture helps the pores of the skin to close, stopping the oozing of oil to the surface. Initially, the pores shrink and finally the skin is smooth. The oils and dead cells which have collected over a day are washed, or scrubbed off, when the dried pack is washed off.

There are several other factors which are associated with acne. One is dandruff. Dandruff has been known not only to cause acne but also to aggravate the condition. If there is any dandruff, it should be treated along with acne, with preparations containing appropriate medications and antiseptics.

The success of the treatment also depends on following some dietary regulations. Being careless about your diet, eating too many sweets, fried and spicy foods has a lot to do with the flaring up of the condition. Avoid sweets, chocolates, confectionary items, ice-cream and aerated drinks. Seafood, like shrimps and lobsters, and red meats are also undesirable.

There are plenty of wholesome, delicious foods that you can enjoy and there is no reason to feel deprived or to starve yourself. You can eat fish, lean meats, vegetables, fresh fruits, cottage cheese, yoghurt and drink six to eight glasses of water daily. You will find that these foods help your bowel habits and prevent constipation. In fact, improper bodily functions, like constipation, contribute to the activity of the oil glands and are linked with dietary faults.

Another aspect of this condition is the emotional state of the acne patient. As it is, adolescence is a time when in search for an identity, the teenager faces several adjustment problems and very often a loss of confidence. During menopause and the pre-menopausal stage, women go through a period of stress, emotional tensions and anxieties. Add to this a face pimpled with eruptions or pitted with scars—and the picture of misery is complete. In fact, emotional stress aggravates an acne condition because it provokes further activity of the oil glands.

The entire treatment of acne is based on a regular programme and depends on how well you can understand the condition and adhere to instructions. A total cure can be achieved, but what is required is unflagging loyalty to routine.

Beauty is a matter of regular care and if you maintain regular hours, get plenty of sleep, eat sensibly, get adequate relaxation, take exercise and strive for freedom from nervous strain, your attitude would definitely be positive towards achieving a cure.

Unmask Your Beauty

ONE of the oldest forms of beauty treatments is the application of masks for the face and body. History is full of instances of women making use of various natural and organic substances to preserve the youth and beauty of their skin and hair.

Masks have a most stimulating effect, improving blood circulation, toning the muscles, maintaining skin elasticity and porcelaining it, apart from the actual benefits of the products themselves. Through time, these beauty treatments have not only survived, but have been improved upon and their values have been recognised and acknowledged.

In fact, the modern woman has the advantage of specialised knowledge. She can understand the demands of her own skin and hair and learn to treat it accordingly. She can even help herself to the beauty aids that exist in her own home—on the kitchen shelf—and take the help of specialised treatments and cures whenever necessary.

For Oily Skins

SHAMASK: HOMEPACK
SHAYOUTH SHATEX

MIX a teaspoon of honey with one egg white and apply thickly on the face and neck. Leave for seven to ten minutes and wash off.

Mix one teaspoon yeast, one teaspoon sugar and half a cup of warm milk, cover and keep in a warm place. When it ferments, use it as a mask.

Mix two tablespoons papaya pulp with 10 drops of lemon juice. Leave it on for 20 minutes and rinse well.

Wash dried peas and dry them in the shade. When absolutely dry, powder and store in a glass jar. Take a little of this powder, add rose water to make a paste. Use as face pack.

Take juice of the pulp of any fruit (orange, sweet lime, watermelon or papaya) and apply on the face as a mask. This is very relaxing. It cleanses the skin, closes pores and stimulates blood circulation.

For Dry Skins

SHAWEEDS SHAYOUTH
SHAPEEL SHAMASK
SHATEX HOMEPACK

TAKE one tablespoon olive oil and mix with two tablespoons of fresh cream. Leave it on the face for 10 minutes. Remove with cotton wool pads soaked in warm water.

To one tablespoon honey, add 15 drops of orange juice, one tablespoon fuller's earth and one tablespoon rose water. Mix well and apply on face. Wash off after 10 minutes.

Mix well one tablespoon each of cornflakes, almond and olive oil or fresh cream. Apply on the face and leave it on for 10 minutes. Then rinse well.

Many herbal extracts have been used in specialised treatment in the form of masks. Among these are the honey apricot peel-off pack, seaweed masks, protein packs and acne packs.

Honey-apricot

Apart from the moisturing effect of honey and the firming qualities of apricot, this pack has been used successfully in treatment of facial-hair. Constant use over a period of time, discourages facial hair growth, and removes it.

The pack is applied in an even film on the face. When it dries, it is peeled off, thus weakening the roots of facial hair. At the same time, it helps nourish the skin, leaving it tight and refreshed.

Seaweed masks

Seaweed is said to have a revitalising effect on the skin, regaining and maintaining the smooth, healthy appearance of a youthful skin. It is an intensive moisturising treatment, rehydrating the skin, especially the delicate tissues which surround the eye.

The mask also conveys valuable minerals to the skin, preventing the formation of wrinkles and promoting blood circulation. Dull, dehydrated skins would benefit most from seaweed treatment.

Protein pack

This is another specialised treatment, containing natural proteins and sandalwood. It not only makes the skin firm and smooth, but also helps deep cleanse it. It provides the skin with nourishment, retexturising it and giving it a new lease of life. It also helps in tissue building and accelerating the cell renewal process.

Acne packs

Oily, rashy and acne conditions require special masks which contain extracts of eucalyptus, clove and sandalwood. These are all antiseptic treatments, which have curative properties, at the same time preventing the spread of infection.

When we talk of the skin, we not only mean the facial skin. The skin is all pervading. That is why many herbal and organic extracts have been used for body care, to improve the quality of the skin on our body and to make it firm and smooth.

The skin has a fantastic capacity to absorb the valuable nutrients that are applied on it. Many body packs have been developed to tighten sagging skin and flabby pores and are being used in health clinics, side by side with slimming and health programmes.

Among these is the Reviva body pack. It contains bael, date extract and pure honey and has a firming effect on the skin. The pack has been used very successfully in improving a sagging bustline. It also helps remove wrinkles, tightens the pores and generally firms up the body.

Where body care is concerned, there have been fascinating developments with herbal extracts. One such treatment is for the bustline, which is being carried out in my health clinic.

The treatment begins with a massage of the breasts with a turmeric-based cream. The idea is that alternating hot and cold therapy would have a stimulating effect on the skin. When the cream is massaged, heat is generated. Immediately after this, an extremely cold brassière is worn. It has pads containing herbal ingredients which are kept frozen at a very low temperature. The herbal extracts used maintain low temperature for a long time.

The hot and cold therapy helps make the skin firm. After this, the body pack is applied and washed off when it dries. The treatment is rounded off with another massage, using an apricot based cream, which has skin firming qualities.

The turmeric cream which is used at the beginning also has other properties which benefit the skin. Turmeric not only has antiseptic virtues, but has a gentle depilatory action on the skin, making it soft, smooth and hair-free.

Combined with lemon, it cleanses the skin very effectively and forms a screen between the drying effect of chlorinated water and the skin. In fact, it can be used on the entire body as a pre-bath treatment.

Rose extract has also been used as a body pack and as a hair-food treatment. The hair can also be treated with various herbal extracts.

Henna is perhaps the oldest known treatments for the hair. Today several other herbs like amla, shikakai, bael and reetha are being combined with henna into special powders, to be mixed into pastes for hair treatments.

Henna has a wonderful conditioning effect on the hair, giving it a sheen and making it more manageable. It is also known to accelerate hair growth and can therefore be used in treatments of hair loss.

For those, who would not like the rich colour imparted by henna, I have incorporated several other ingredients into a hair-conditioning powder, which can be used instead of henna, or along with it. This combination acts as a deep cleanser, maintains the natural moisture balance of the scalp and makes the hair stronger and healthier.

Henna not only has a beneficial effect on the hair, but also on the skin. When it is combined with lactic acid, it does not impart colour at all. Keeping this in mind, I have used henna even in a skin-food cream.

Skin Rejuvenation

DERMATOLOGISTS and cosmetologists agree that the skin that has been properly cared for, stays youthful for a longer time. The converse is also true. Neglected skins develop the symptoms of ageing prematurely. In other words, the right kind of preventive care helps to preserve the youth of the skin. Today, cosmetology techniques offer corrective techniques, in the form of external care, after ageing changes have appeared on the skin.

Helena Rubenstein said: "The skin has a tremendous capacity for self-rejuvenation if properly cared for". A mature skin develops certain particular characteristics. The skin cells are dry, having lost the ability to retain moisture. This is apparent on the outer layer of the skin, which develops fine lines. The cells of the outer layer are dry and shrivelled, giving the skin a rough texture. The problem of moisture loss is aggravated by a decrease in oil-gland activity. Therefore, there is a lack of both moisture and oil. Most aged skins also show a tendency for cellular build-up, when the excess skin cells accumulate on the surface, coarsening the skin texture. This may be accompanied by an increase of pigment, which accumulates in a patchy manner. Another important change that takes place is a loss of elasticity and resilience. The stage is set for the lines and wrinkles to appear. These symptoms may also appear through neglect of daily care.

Corrective measures must be such, which seek to restore suppleness to the skin and make it smooth, resilient and moist, with an even colour tone. This is a time when professional guidance is required. Specialized treatments can be undertaken under professional supervision, along with advice on the routine care of the skin.

Weekly facial toning treatments help to revitalise the skin. Professional massage with rejuvenating creams and exposure to certain gadgets benefit the skin and also make it more receptive to the methods employed. The massage stimulates oil-gland activity and blood circulation and also tones up the facial muscles. The basic functions of the skin improve. Facial massages also induce relaxation and this helps skin receptivity. Treatments today involve the use of specialized beauty gadgets that improve the functions of the skin cells either by increasing absorption and penetration, or by drawing out impurities.

Combating dryness is an integral part. In order to improve the skin's ability to receive moisturising treatments, the cellular build-up on the skin surface must be removed. This is done by the use of specialised masks. When the build-up is excessive, other methods are employed to refine the skin. Intensive moisturisation methods should be used to correct the effects of dehydration, as well as to protect the skin from further depletion of moisture. If the skin has acquired pigmented blotches, the treatment is adjusted to produce an even colour tone. A sunscreen should also be used to protect the skin from further damage.

The thermoherb mask and the vegetable peel are two of the specialized skin rejuvenating treatments that have produced good results. The thermoherb mask is a mini face-lift. The ingredients include extracts of various herbs that are known to revitalize the skin. The mask hardens on the skin, creating an ideal temperature between itself and the skin, at which the skin's capacity to absorb the products are heightened. The mask comes off in one-piece, leaving the skin tighter and porcelained. The vegetable peel follows a gentle dermabrasive process to refine the skin.

Research with plant products has enabled the isolation of ingredients that help to alleviate old age symptoms. Many of these have been formulated into cosmetic aids. Among these are powerful rehydrants like cactus, aloe vera, seaweed and ginseng. Extracts of almond, apricot, cabbage, carrot, wheat-germ have been used in nourishing creams to stimulate cell activity, encourage moisture retention and provide 'skin food'.

HOME FACIAL

1. Cleanse with Cactus Aloe

2. Massage in Skin Food

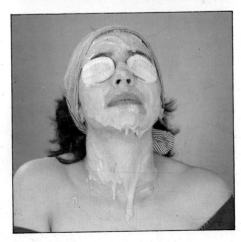

3. Apply mask, use Cucumber slices to perk up eyes.

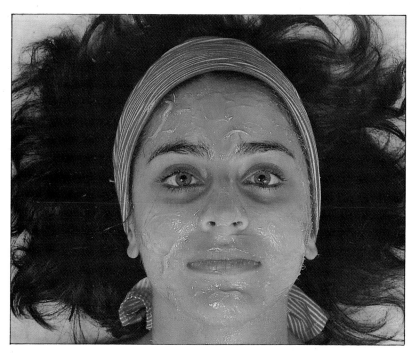

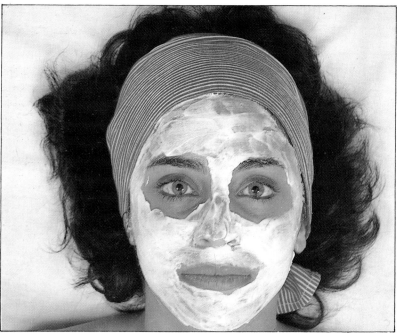

THERMOHERB MASK

*Cleanse with Cactus Aloe
Skin Food Application*

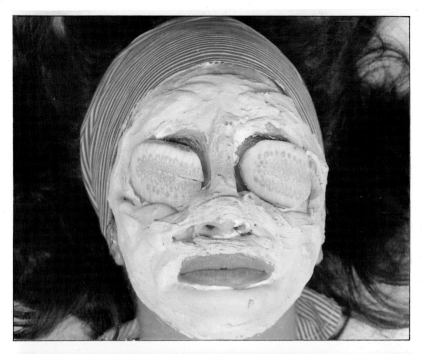

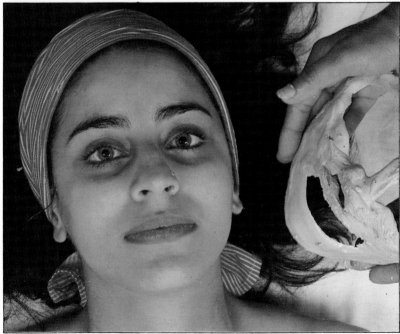

Apply the mask
When dry lift off the mask

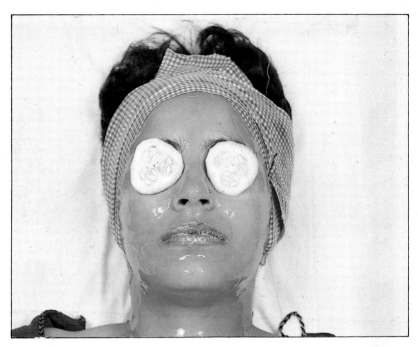

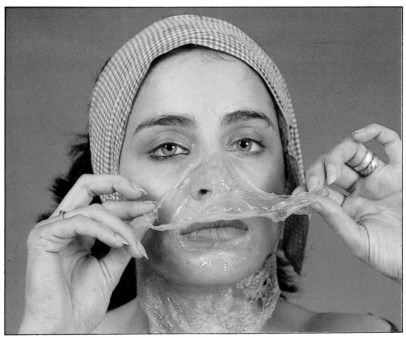

APRICOT PEEL OFF MASK

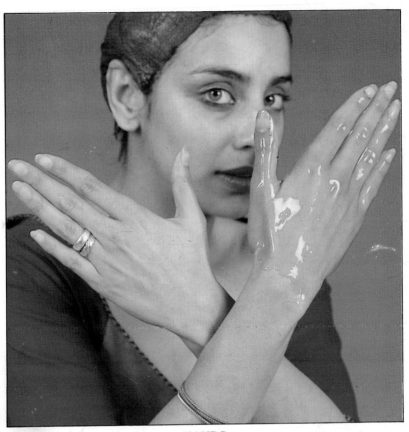

HANDS
*Apricot peel of mask to give your
hands a lift up!*

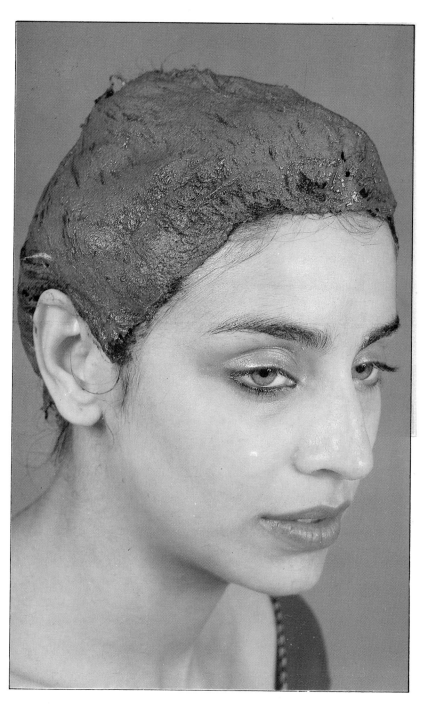

HENNA APPLICATION

Shahnaz Husain

Certain areas of the skin are more vulnerable to ageing. The area around the eyes and the neck require particular attention. The skin around the eyes is very thin and needs creams that are light in texture. Almond creams are ideal for this region. The daily skin care routine should involve the application of the cream for a few minutes. It should then be removed gently with moist cotton wool. Masks are normally not applied around the eyes, but a special seaweed mask has been formulated for this delicate area. Light and watery in consistency, it is easy to apply and remove, so that no stretching or pulling of the skin is involved. The neck should be included in the daily nourishing routine, with the use of the face mask. The neck usually suffers due to neglect.

Maintenance in the form of daily skin care is most important. This benefits the skin surface as the outer layer has the capacity of self replacement. It is on this capacity that the life of the skin depends. Daily moisturisation and nourishment, with weekly professional care would help as protective, preventive and corrective treatments. With the skin there is one advantage—it will respond to care.

Skin Years

WE are born with soft, smooth, flawless skins. As time passes and we grow older, the skin, like other organs of the body ages too—only more so, as it is exposed to environmental factors. The skin, like us, goes through several phases, during which it may be susceptible to problems that mar its soft, natural beauty.

During the pre-teen years, the skin maintains its natural texture. Children approaching the teens should be made aware of the importance of cleanliness and hygiene. They should learn the basics about skin health, as well as the importance of diet and exercise. With the onset of puberty, the skin which behaved so well, starts giving trouble. The hormonal activity in the body affects the sebaceous glands, resulting in excessive oil secretions. The skin begins to look greasy and sallow. The pores become enlarged due to the increased flow of oil, which can harden and collect in the pores. This gives rise to blackheads, spots, pimples and acne. Acne is, in fact, associated with adolescence.

The teenager should learn to follow an appropriate cleansing routine, to keep the pores free of clogged grease. The excessive use of alkaline soaps should be discouraged, as they leave the skin predisposed to bacterial attacks. The use of medicated soaps and cleansing grains would help to prevent acne infections. When acne is present, professional advice should be sought in good time, so that the condition does not get out of control.

After the teens and into the twenties, the skin gradually settles down, with the decrease in glandular activity. During the twenties and thirties, the skin is usually at its best, unless it has been neglected earlier. Basic skin care during this time should be geared towards maintenance, so that the skin does not acquire the signs of premature ageing. During the twenties, women increase the use of make-up cosmetics and this requires regular skin care. Some of these cosmetics can cause a lack of moisture in the skin, which if allowed to persist, hastens the appearance of lines and wrinkles. All make-up should be removed before bedtime, so that the skin is allowed to 'breathe'. The cell renewal process is at its best when we sleep and should be allowed to proceed efficiently. The youthful quality of the skin depends on this.

After the age of twenty-five, regular facial massages help to preserve the elasticity and resilience of the skin. Professional cleansing and massage keep the skin free of impurities and maintain muscle tone. The circulation of blood to the surface of the skin is also improved. Daily care routines, in the form of cleansing, nourishing and moisturising protect the skin from the ravages of time. It also improves the skin's normal functions and increases its capacity to combat the factors that can spoil its beauty.

The twenties and thirties are also the child bearing years. During pregnancy, many skin problems can occur due to hormonal or uterine disbalances. Chloasma or the 'pregnancy mask' is quite common. It consists of pigmented patches on the cheeks, nose and forehead. These pigmented areas can also become dry and rough. The use of protective 'sunscreen' creams with intensive moisturising is helpful.

Daily moisturisation is a most important part of skin care during the thirties, when the skin begins to lose its capacity to hold moisture. The area around the eyes needs special care with the use of almond based under-eye creams. Heavy creams should not be applied on this area. Careful cleansing with a rehydrant cleansing gel, using moist cotton wool is advocated. Protective and preventive care are an integral part of the daily routine.

The skin that has had regular care will not show its age at forty. However, most people do neglect their skins in terms of regularity. Lines and wrinkles manifest themselves at this age, in the form of 'crow's feet' and laughter lines. Very often, during the forties, a particular kind of acne may occur, due to stress, or decreased estrogen secretions. The skin takes on a flushed look with blackheads and small pimples, for which professional care becomes necessary.

Menopause, or the actual cessation of the menstrual flow may take place between the ages of 48 and 53. Many women go through acute mental depression and emotional stress at this time. This can often cause skin problems. But, menopause itself does not produce the signs of ageing. Rather, the look of the skin is influenced by other factors like diet, rest, exercise and skin care. It is natural to fear the loss of youth and beauty, but the woman who has a healthy body and a positive mental outlook is one who has taken good care of herself. She faces the fifties with the minimum of distress.

Loss of elasticity and dryness are the main problems of a mature skin. Poor blood circulation can also cause deterioration in skin colour and tone. Regular massage and nourishment can improve this condition. Pigmented spots and patches are also common. Cellular build-up is yet another problem, causing the skin to look thick and coarse. Specialised face masks can help remove cellular build-up. The regular skin-care routine should be adjusted to include more moisturising methods. A pre-bath gel applied on the skin before washing, protects it from the drying effects of soap and water washing.

A light moisturiser should be applied as a make-up base. Make-up foundations should be of the creamy variety to keep the skin emollient. Mature skins can be very sensitive. If this is the case, even greater care is needed. The use of soap may have to be discontinued. Soothing packs can help the skin, with moisturisation. A rehydrant cleansing gel should be used instead of soap.

The right kind of care can maintain and also restore to the skin a softer, more moist quality that is so characteristic of youth. With skin care, it is never too early, or too late to start.

The Pigmentation Problem

SHAWHITE SHAFAIR
SHABLEM SHABRIGHT

THE skin has wonderful protective responses. In the deeper layers of the epidermis are cells which produce melanin—a pigment that gives the skin its colour. Melanin protects the skin from the rays of the sun. When the skin is exposed to the sun, the production of melanin increases. Once it is produced, melanin matures and moves into the upper layers of the epidermis. In some skins, this transfer of melanin gets blocked and there is no pigmentation. On the other hand, the transfer is accelerated, resulting in pigmentation and dark skins.

In fair skins, melanin gets gradually destroyed as it moves upwards towards the horny layer of the epidermis. In dark skins, the destruction of melanin does not continue as far as the superficial layer. Therefore, the skin surface in dark skins contains much more melanin. As melanin is a dark pigment, the skin surface acquires a dark colour. More the melanin, darker is the skin.

Internal pathological problems can sometimes interfere with the production or transfer of melanin. This may give rise to skin problems associated with colour, in the form of white or dark patches. Exposure to sun increases the production of melanin. When the transfer is affected, it may be uneven, giving rise to pigmented patches. Repeated exposure to sun causes the patches to become more persistent.

Skin pigmentation has been treated successfully by external treatments, which involve production of a more even colour tone, as well as improvement of skin texture. Very often, skin pigmentation is accompanied by cellular build-up on the outer layer, which already contains pigment. This is very common on mature skins. Therefore, the treatment is geared towards removal of cellular build-up, apart from skin protection.

Since exposure to sun increases the production of melanin, the skin must be protected. Cosmetic products which protect the skin against the sun are called 'sunscreens'. They contain substances that block out the harmful part of the sun's rays. When choosing a sunscreen, we should keep two aspects in mind—first it should block out the sun's rays effectively and secondly, it should help to avoid dehydration of the skin. In many cases, chemical sunscreens have given rise to irritative reactions, while natural products have not only eliminated this problem, but have also promoted healing. A sunscreen containing sandalwood is an ideal protection against the sun. Combined with a honey based moisturiser, it forms an invisible film on the face.

Skin pigmentation has been clinically treated. This involves a course of treatments to hydrate and revitalise the skin, with the removal of pigmented patches. Specialized masks are used to remove the cellular build-up and bring forth a more even colour tone. The removal of the dead epithelial cells activates the skin to step up the replacement of dead cells with healthy ones. The purpose is also to remove the excess surface cells that contain pigment. Thus, the skin's texture and contour improve and gradually the skin becomes more translucent and much smoother. Rehydration of the skin also becomes much easier, once the cellular build-up is removed.

The daily-care routine should also be adjusted to deal with the problem. This includes choosing products that help to lighten the patches. Some chemical ingredients that have been used to lighten skin colour have had adverse reactions. In many cases, they have reacted to sunlight and increased pigmentation. Products containing natural extracts have eliminated this risk. The daily routine should also lay an emphasis on moisturisation. In cases when there is excessive dryness of the skin, the use of harsh soaps should be discontinued. A pre-bath gel containing turmeric and lemon can be applied before washing the face. Turmeric has healing properties and also lightens skin colour.

Cleanse the skin in the morning and at bedtime with a rehydrant cleanser. One that contains extracts of aloe, cactus and lemon is excellent. Protect the skin with a sunscreen base during the day. At night, the skin should be nourished after cleansing and wiped off with moist cotton wool. A medicated ointment is prescribed for use on the pigmented patches. This is left on all night. A daily face mask is also prescribed. Sometimes, a combination of masks is used. Among these are placenta masks, which reduce the effects of sun damage. In fact, this mask has been used to treat sunburn, which is common on fair skins. When intensive moisturisation is required, masks containing seaweed can be used. These masks are prescribed once or twice a week, with the daily face mask, depending on individual requirements. One such daily face mask consists of a herbal powder that is to be mixed with honey, yoghurt and egg white. A seaweed lotion is also added. Seaweeds are powerful natural moisturisers and have great therapeutic value.

The correction of skin problems has become a part of modern cosmetology. Treatments have become highly specialized and beauty is being viewed from the curative aspect. Beauty therapy today is based on protective, preventive and corrective care. Together, they represent the foundation of modern cosmetology.

Sun vs Skin   *SHABASE*

DURING Victorian times, much emphasis was laid on pale, lily-white skins and women would never expose themselves to the sun. Now, a golden glow or rich tawny complexions are admired and women chase the sun to tan their skins. In India, a high premium is placed on a 'fair' skin. Right through the ups and downs of fashion trends and following blindly whatever is 'in', we have ignored the fact that the sun, which is such a great benefactor in every other way, is the skin's greatest enemy. Many dermatologists believe that nothing wroughts as much damage on the skin as the sun.

From this aspect, fair skins are actually at a disadvantage. The darker the skin, the more resistant it is to the damaging effects of the sun, although dark skins are not immune to it. A dark skin contains more melanin, which actually protects the skin against the sun's rays. Sunlight has the capacity to penetrate the skin. It not only affects the surface, but also the living tissues of the lower layers. A few days of intense exposure can produce symptoms of ageing. Sun exposure causes definite changes in the skin and can even predispose it to cancer.

The most damaging effect of the sun on the skin is that it dehydrates it, causing it to become dry, rough and wrinkled. Freckles, pigmented spots and patches also occur. An immediate reaction is the expansion of blood vessels. That is why the skin looks flushed and red after sun-exposure. Gradually, it gets tanned. The sun also damages the supporting fibres of the skin. The result of all these effects is premature ageing. A certain dermatologist is of the opinion that the sun is good only for children, who require sunlight for the metabolism of Vitamin D.

Protection of the skin against the sun's rays is the only way to delay the ageing signs. This entails the use of an effective sunscreen whenever exposure to the sun is inevitable. Long exposure should be avoided as far as possible. A sunscreen would not only block out the harmful part of the sun's rays, but would also prevent loss of moisture. Replacing moisture loss is also important. The use of rehydrant cleansers, moisturising creams and masks would give back to the skin the moisture that is lost, keeping it soft and smooth. Sun damage can also be reversed with intensive moisturisation techniques and products that help to soothe the skin and revitalize it. Neglect of daily care would only aggravate the problem, leading to damage that cannot be reversed, if at all with a great deal of time, money and effort. Through lack of awareness and neglect, you can be your skin's greatest enemy.

Some Common Beauty Problems

SHAWHITE
SHABLEM
SHAFAIR

FRECKLES: The skin has its own protective mechanism against sunlight. When it is exposed to the rays of the sun, the pigment in the skin increases in order to protect the inner layer of the skin. Repeated exposure to the sun especially for long durations, causes the skin to tan. In fair skins, there is an accumulation of pigment in the lower layers, which gets gradually destroyed, as it is transferred to the upper layers. When there is excessive exposure, fair skins acquire freckles, which are accumulation of pigments, with areas that have little or no pigment. Freckles are tiny dark spots sprinkled on the face. They appear on areas that are more elevated—like the nose, cheek bones, and forehead.

If your skin has the tendency to freckle, you should avoid excessive exposure to the sun. You should always protect your skin, whenever exposure to the sun is inevitable, by using a 'sunscreen'. Freckles can be lightened by the use of special skin care products. Lemon and turmeric are two natural products that lighten skin colour. A freckled skin would also need intensive moisturisation with the help of cleansers, creams and masks containing extracts of aloe, cactus, seaweed. Anti-freckle lotions and ointments would also help.

Whiteheads: Like blackheads, these are caused by the accumulation of hardened sebum or oil, in the pores of the skin. The difference is that in areas where the skin is fine and delicate, the clogged grease is not exposed to the air. Oxidisation does not take place and darkens the tips, as in the case of blackheads. The whiteheads appear in the form of tiny, pearly, white raised spots. They are common on the area just above the cheekbones, where the skin is fine. On oily skins, they may appear as part of a 'problem skin condition', with blackheads, pimples and acne.

Deep pore cleansing with beauty grains helps to discourage them. The mixture of beauty grains and skin tonic is rubbed gently on the affected areas, before being rinsed off with water. The gentle dermabrasive action discourages their formation and also helps to dislodge them after a period of time.

Whiteheads should never be removed forcibly, even with a blac extractor. In the case of whiteheads, or milia, as they are called, the pore is not open. Forcible removal will only damage skin tissue and cause infections. With external care, you should include adequate amounts of fresh fruits and vegetables in your daily diet. Drink plenty of water and fresh fruit juices. A glass of warm water with the juice of a lemon, helps to cleanse the body of toxic residues and improves the elimination of wastes.

Dark under-eye circles: This is a common problem, which is caused by lack of sleep, fatigue, stress, dietary deficiency or disease. It is generally easy to spot people with chronic insomnia by the tell-tale circles around the eyes. Sleep is very essential both to health and beauty. If insomnia is your problem, or you suffer from chronic fatigue, you must consult your doctor. With medical help, you should follow a daily beauty routine. Remember that the skin around the eyes is very delicate. Choose your cosmetic products with care. Every night, cleanse the skin around the eyes with a rehydrant gel, using moist cotton wool. Then apply an under-eye cream. Products that are used around the eyes must be very light in texture. An under-eye cream, containing lanolin and almond is ideal. Almond helps to remove dark circles as it is a mild natural bleach. It is also an excellent 'skin food'. Remove the cream with moist cotton wool after ten minutes. No cream should be left on the skin around the eyes for long periods.

Avoid the area around the eyes when you apply face masks. Only those that are especially formulated for this region should be used. One of these is a seaweed mask, in liquid form. It is of a light texture and of a watery consistency, forming a light film on the skin. It can be easily removed with water. Seaweed is a moisturiser and also has a revitalising effect on the skin.

Enlarged Pores: The over activity of the sebaceous glands usually results in a skin with enlarged pores. Oil is secreted by these glands through the pores of the skin. Excessive secretion of oil causes the pores to be clogged. The pores are thus stretched to accommodate the hardened sebum and lose their natural resilience. Excessive secretion of oil, can thicken the pores and mar the porcelain quality of skin. The skin becomes coarse. The pores must be kept free of sebum, so that they do not get enlarged. The use of a medicated cleanser helps to reduce surface oil. Deep pore cleansing with specialised cleansers also helps. One containing ginseng, cleanses the pores and refines them. The skin should be toned daily. A skin tonic with a rose base is excellent. Keep some in a bowl in the refrigerator. Soak cotton wool pads and pat the skin briskly with it after the cleansing routine. You may use it several times a day to reduce oiliness. Extract of rose helps to close the pores and benefits the texture of the skin.

Warts: These are small, hard, raised growths, with a rough surface, that appear on any part of the body. They are common on the hands and face. It is believed that they are caused by a virus entering the skin.

There may be a single wart, or they may appear in clusters of several tiny growths. Many remedies have been tried, many of which do not ensure prevention of regrowth. A wart should never be picked in an attempt to get rid of it. It is wiser to seek professional advice, since wart removal methods are available.

A successful method of removing warts is by the introduction of a specialized product into the area. This stops the blood supply to the wart. Gradually it dries up and crumbles. Ointments and creams are also used to control the infection. The treatment of warts is conducted by a specially trained person and is known as sclerotherapy.

Under-eye bags: This is usually a hereditary problem. They appear like pouches just under the eyes and seem to add years to the face. It is usually during the thirties that under-eye bags develop and become apparent. Sometimes, these pouches may be caused by other reasons— like sinus, urinary tract infections and kidney ailments. The skin has a tendency to accumulate fluid. Since the skin around the eyes is very thin and delicate, it has very little resilience. When it stretches, it begins to sag. If you suffer from any internal problems, do seek medical help. It is also important to keep the kidneys functioning well by taking adequate quantities of water. This helps to 'flush' the system. The kidneys help to remove toxins and other waste substances from the body. Decrease your intake of coffee and tea. Drink a glass of warm water with the juice of a lemon, first thing in the morning. It is said that about one-and-a-half litres of fluid is necessary to keep the kidneys functioning well. A major part of this should be plain water.

Never apply heavy creams around the eyes, or leave any cream on for long durations. This increases puffiness. Potato extract, or slices can be applied around the eyes to reduce puffiness. Cucumber juice can also be applied. Stubborn eye-bags that are hereditary may be removed by cosmetic surgery.

Stretch marks: As the name suggests, these marks are caused by over stretching of the skin, destroying its elasticity and resilience. These marks develop when weight loss follows weight gain. That is why they are so common after pregnancy. The skin on the abdomen stretches during pregnancy. After confinement, long marks appear on the skin. These are light in colour and stretch over quite a large expanse of skin. These marks are not on the surface, but are actually caused by cracks in the elastic fibres below. Stretch marks may also develop on the breasts, thighs and upper arms.

The best treatment for stretch marks is preventive care, since it is impossible to remove the marks entirely once they have formed. Massage a pre-bath cream into the skin daily on the abdomen and breasts. This should be started as early as possible, before the skin begins to stretch. This helps to keep the skin supple and improves its elasticity, helping it to protect itself better. The massage should be continued for a few months after the delivery. It is better to use creams that contain ingredients which maintain the resilience of the skin and are also easily absorbed by it. Extracts of turmeric, lemon and apricot have proved useful. Apricot has an astringent action on the skin. It is also essential to keep the skin well moisturised. During the later months, the skin may become very dry and itchy. If you scratch the skin to relieve the itching, further damage can be caused. Natural extracts also help to soothe skin and keep it free from rashy or irritative conditions. Some of them also improve the colour tone of the skin. Creams which have a protein content will benefit skin tissue, while body packs may be used to maintain natural elasticity.

Regular massages can help to make stretch marks less apparent. Those who are over-weight and are planning to go on a slimming course should pay particular heed to this problem and adopt daily care routines to avoid it. Any slimming programme should be accompanied by regular massage of the areas that are vulnerable to stretch marks.

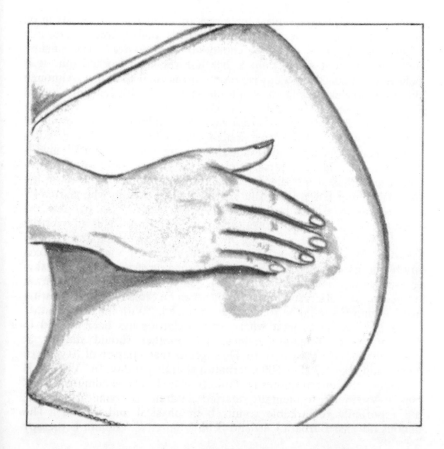

The Phenomenon of Vitamin E

THE benefits of Vitamin E, as far as beauty is concerned, have been the subject of much controversy and most scientists prefer not to commit themselves. However, it is known that anti-oxidants like Vitamin E help to preserve purity in such things as butter and slow down the deterioration of leather and rubber. Its use may, therefore, help to preserve the skin from the normal ageing process of the body to some extent. The proponents of Vitamin E therapy say that it has softening qualities, minimising wrinkles and making lines less conspicuous. During the last Beauty Congress I attended, American nutritionists claimed that it helped to control acne scars, angina, ulcers, stretch marks, varicose veins and pigmentation. Basically, they placed the importance on the anti-oxidant properties of Vitamin E for controlling and delaying ageing of the skin. It is known to be contained in foods like beef, liver, green peas, vegetable oils, eggs, turnip and sunflower oil. If most of these are present in the diet, supplementing by capsule is not necessary.

Martindale's pharmaceutical bible says of Vitamin E: "It occurs in oil from soyabeans, in wheat germ, cotton seeds, maize, green leaves like lettuce. Soyabean is the most commonly used source". The smallest daily requirement of Vitamin E has not yet been worked out. It is believed that 10–30 mg a day is present in a normal adult diet. Although there are no clearly defined symptoms which specially demand Vitamin E, it is strongly advocated by doctors for muscular dystrophy, controlling abortions and cardio-vascular conditions. The results of Vitamin E therapy have been controversial. It was first discovered in 1932, when it was tested and found that rats on a diet without Vitamin E aborted, while the male rats became sterile. Hence, there was the wave that science has at last discovered a 'fertility capsule'. Pioneers in the use of Vitamin E were the Shute Brothers of London, who started by treating cardiovascular problems with it. By 1954, 15,000 patients had been treated and their findings were published in journals all over the world. W. Shute, the co-author of "Vitamin E for Ailing and Healthy Hearts," showed slides of the beneficial effects of Vitamin E, taken orally and used topically. He proved reasonable success in leukoplakia (pre-cancerous condition of the skin), diabetic gangrene, injury from burns, etc. It is interesting to note that when Dr Shute was asked at what age Vitamin E should be started, he answered. "With the first breath!" Cases have come to light where arteriosclerosis has been noticed in new-born and premature babies. The mother should start it at pregnancy and the baby at birth. He suggests that a person of 70 years of age should take 1,200–1,600 international units per day. In "Vitamin E Pioneers", the author quotes Dr Guidice, who has been administering 2 gms of Vitamin E to mentally retarded children, as saying "Vitamin E has reportedly remarkable results both physical and mental". The famous novelist Barbara Cartland is an admirer of Vitamin E therapy and says. "It really is the vitality vitamin. It keeps one young and is marvellous for old people. It helps oxygenate the tissues and is essential for metabolising the fatty acids of the body". She says that she became interested in Vitamin E when doing voluntary work in distressed areas. "There was a high rate of miscarriages among the poorly nourished young women. Given Vitamin E, they responded beautifully. It is fantastic for the skin, in capsule form or applied on the skin as a cream.

In my opinion, Vitamin E requirement depends on the individual needs of a person, keeping demands and age in mind. It does have healing and skin beautifying properties. What is important to note is that it is a water soluble vitamin and excess intake is excreted. I have found that skin care with a Vitamin E cream keeps at bay certain problems, like wrinkles and crow's feet. It helps to keep the skin smooth and preserve its youth. It is interesting to note that there is a difference between the synthetic version available in the market and the natural one. There are two kinds of natural Vitamin E:d-alpha tocopherol acetate (oil form) and d-alpha tocopherol succinate (powder form).

I find that Vitamin E is being prescribed by gynaecologists for women who complain of melanin disbalance and chloasma conditions, or to ward off miscarriages. Several of my clients react beautifully to Vitamin E, used in a marrow pack, for clearing chronic pigmentation, blemishes and wrinkles. In the beauty world, it is used for firming the breasts, softening the skin, in nourishing creams, hair tonics, and shampoos. Is it a wonder vitamin? Scientists are still working on it and hope to find an answer in the near future.

Seaweed Therapy

**SHAWEEDS
SHAFRESH**

IN the domain of Beauty and Cosmetology, surprisingly beneficial results have been seen in certain treatments with seaweed, in case of falling hair, dandruff, acne, skin eruptions, cellulitis, development and firming of the breasts, slimming and the rejuvenation of the skin. The early Greeks had referred to it as 'Thalassotherapia'. 'Thalassa' means the 'sea' and 'therapia' means to cure. In the 16th century, seaweed was used for the treatment of goitre, lung ailments and even premature deliveries. In the world of today, seaweed has been known to have beneficial properties in the sphere of medicine, not only in the achievement of cures, but, in the fact that being a natural herbal therapy, the harmful effect of modern day drugs can be eliminated.

Seaweed can be defined as a vegetable, containing chlorophyl, without roots or structure, found in sea water. They are living organisms which belong to the plant world. They consist of identical cells and their growth is effected by osmosis from cell to cell. Their growth and development is dependent on the mineral elements found in the sea. Seaweeds reproduce annually by spores. It is also interesting to note that the actual count of varieties of seaweed, at present, is 865. Recent research has revealed the existence of female phytohormones in seaweed, which were not known till now. The amount of phytohormones cannot be measured, but the comparative results in cosmetology and agriculture are an index to the relative amounts found in the different varieties of seaweed. Seaweed also has the remarkable property of staying fresh and retaining 95 per cent of its properties if gathered and treated without leaving its natural environment.

Certain elements in seaweed allow the skin to assimilate phosphorous and calcium, which stimulate the skin cells. Consequently, the skin has a better resistance towards infections, can fight against its own natural decadence and can conserve itself better. Seaweed contains all the active elements found in a live cell, like nitrogen, phosphorous, sulphur, calcium, potassium and magnesium. They contain all the elemental bodies, bacterial and antibiotic, due to the presence of acrylic acid. In order to be beneficial, seaweed must be collected from deep-sea waters, because shallow waters are usually polluted and the weeds lose 60 to 70 per cent of their properties.

People who consume sea products are less prone to certain diseases than others, simply because marine water contains the elements and minerals which are so valuable. Marine plant life is found in areas which are rich in minerals and clams, fish, oysters, depend on seaweed for their survival, absorbing and retaining all the minerals. Seaweed, therefore, constitutes more than 25 per cent of the diet of the Japanese and in many sea bound countries it is also eaten. Some elements contained in seaweed are also found in the human organism, such as:

* Sodium chloride: Maintains the equilibrium of acids.
* Iodine: Important for the proper functioning of the thyroid, blood, arteries, ageing process and fatigue.
* Potassium: Stimulates at times of stress.
* Copper, zinc and manganese: Maintain the equilibrium of glands.
* Magnesium: Helps the defence organism.

Since seaweed contains these minerals, it can be used for the treatment of the following:

Insomnia
Nervous disorders
Glandular troubles
Demineralisation (digestive troubles, constipation and diarrhoea)
Anaemia
Regularisation of the thyroid
Chronic rheumatism

Depression
Circulatory problems of the blood
Irregular menstrual cycles

It is an accepted fact that all these problems lead to beauty, skin and hair problems. The treatment of the root causes would eliminate the problems in the beauty sphere. In aesthetics and cosmetology, seaweed has been effectively used in the treatment of the following:

Obesity
Ageing
Regeneration of cells and tissues
Circulatory problems
Broken nails
Varicose veins
Cellulitis
Dermatosis
Acne seborrhoea
Falling hair
Rejuvenation of the skin
Beauty masks

The Skin: The skin which has been well nourished, free of toxins, well balanced and well mineralised, does not suffer any problem and is in a good condition to resist elements which could attack it. The action of seaweed on certain bacterial diseases (acne) is spectacular. On the other hand the chlorophyl content helps photosynthesis, which helps to nourish the cells. This advantage can be best seen in the effects of seaweed beauty masks.

Advantages of seaweed masks:

* achieves the skin balance by rehydrating the epidermis;
* provides the necessary mineral salts, amino acids and Vitamins A,B,C,D and E;
* penetrates the skin by osmosis;
* makes the skin supple, soft, smooth and firm;
* suits all types of skins;
* closes open pores;
* tones up flabby tissues and has a remarkable effect on wrinkles of the neck and under-eye bags;
* improves blood circulation by having internally cleansing effects;
* clears up dark spots by achieving an equilibrium in oily skin and other problems; and
* has an effect on the life of the epidermis and helps to conserve it.

Treatment of acne by seaweed: Acne usually appears when there is a change in hormonal activity (puberty and menopause).

The areas where it appears would be the forehead, chin, the back and the thorax. The arms and legs are not affected by acne. It usually occurs on seborrhic skins, because the sebaceous glands are stimulated by an excess of the male hormone. Blackheads form due to grease accumulating in a pore and oxidisation of the head. Acne is a generalised problem and not a particular disease. It can occur due to shock which upsets the nervous system, wrong diet, constipation and imbalance of the endocrine glands. Treatment of acne could be either internal metabolic to regulate the organism or an external treatment: as in seaweed masks.

The treatment should begin on the tenth day from the commencement of the menstrual cycle. A decoction of algae (seaweed) should be used, as well as 1½ litres of water taken everyday. This would help to:

eliminate toxins,
achieve skin balance,
remineralise the skin,
decontaminate the skin.

With seaweed treatments, regular sleep, bowel movements and diet are important. There should be a decrease in the intake of sweets, bread and greasy foods. Antibiotics or drugs of the cortisone family are not advisable. Sometimes antibiotics, instead of achieving a cure, aggravate the condition. To cure acne, the hyperactivity of the seabaceous glands should be controlled, for which another hormone will have to be administered. That is why pills rich in oestrogen are an excellent way of treating acne. Similarly, seaweed, due to the presence of phytohormones, enables an effective treatment too.

Seaweed baths: The skin breathes and has a certain permeability. Penetrable baths have existed for a long time. In ancient times, princesses used to take milk baths. Thermal baths have still not been understood scientifically. It would be ideal to take advantage of our natural wealth through sea baths. They should be taken with hot sea water. That is how the idea was conceived of using concentrates or seaweed, which would allow the benefits of the sea at home.

A hot seaweed bath has certain advantages. The heat of the water raises the temperature of the skin. The body relaxes and rids itself of toxic matter and allows the elements in seaweed to penetrate the skin. The increase in body temperature provokes a quicker chemical reaction. Most feminine problems in connection with beauty are due to bad circulation, which, in turn, is connected with the insufficient elimination of toxins.

Seaweed baths are particularly recommended for people who are afflicted by the woes of modern day life, like chronic fatigue, rheumatism, anaemia, old age, obesity, cellulitis. For a beneficial effect, it will be necessary to use the seaweed concentrates in sufficient quantities. A minimum of 15 to 20 baths are needed before any results can be seen. A seaweed bath should be taken every two days.

Certain oils can be combined with seaweed to increase the properties of these baths. For instance, seaweed combined with eucalyptus, arnica, menthol and oil of camphor would tone up the entire system and give it vitality. It can also have a beneficial effect on the respiratory system by disinfecting the lungs.

Slimming with seaweed: Seaweed baths act on fatty tissues in the form of a catalytic agent. To get the maximum results, it is best not to start the treatment when the person is bloated or has put on too much weight, just before menstruation. Seaweed baths give the person a feeling of well being and relief from tension and fatigue. This has a psychological impact which is essential for good results.

The effect of seaweed on the thyroid glands: The thyroid gland secretes thyroxine which kills bacteria and germs in the blood stream and maintains the equilibrium of the metabolism. It controls nervous tension and improves blood circulation by controlling the coagulation of blood. It also helps to eliminate toxins, cholestrol and uric acid and influences the production of hormones. The functioning of the thyroid gland is dependent on iodine. The iodine in seaweed helps to revitalise the entire system through the thyroid gland. Since the most important element in seaweed is iodine, it can be effectively used in treatments and play a big role in the well-being of the body and spirit. As early as 3000 B.C., the Chinese Emperor, Shen Nung, who researched extensively in herbs, referred to the iodine content in seaweed and its use as an effective remedy for various ailments. Lack of iodine causes dryness of the skin and also causes the hair to become dry and brittle. Paradoxically, oversaturation of iodine can provoke malfunctioning of the thyroid gland.

Dr Valnet, who has long propagated the use of seaweed in the sphere of medicine, says that a majority of doctors ignore the innumerable possibilities both medical and biological, to be found in seaweed. In the East and Far East, people have attached much importance to seaweed in their diet, whereas the Western civilisation had until recently ignored its beneficial powers. The depths of the sea can open various avenues in 'Seaweed Therapy' for the benefit of beauty, cosmetology and medicine. It has, after all been said: "Life comes from the sea."

Natural Beauty Aids in Ancient India

THE cult of Beauty is very old. Perhaps as old as time itself. From times immemorial, women have been beautifying themselves by various ways and means, from the days of Cleopatra to our present times.

Indian herbs and natural beauty aids are as ancient as antiquity. For centuries, women in India have been beautifying themselves with every possible natural aid. Our ancient paintings, epics and great works of art are an eloquent testimony to this fact Indian women have used oils of roses, musk, juhi and bela as perfumes. They used shikakai and musk for bubble-baths, when the West could not imagine such a concept. Today the famous salons in Paris charge a hundred dollars for the famous Cleopatra Bath which contains synthetics bubbles and perfumes.

Indian women knew the rare rehydrant value of silt and underwater weeds from running brooks. These combined with the oil of musk, turmeric and geranium was used as a face and body mask...to be washed off with milk when dry. It is these translucent and flawless skins that come alive in the famous Kangra miniatures and the glass paintings of Western India. Even excavations of the Indus Valley Civilization (3000 B.C.) have shown evidence of a wide use of natural cosmetics that women used as embellishments.

The use of pure, concentrated extracts of flowers, leaves, barks, herbs and even wood is what India has always been known for. It is a known fact that India conducted a brisk trade in all these together with her spices and calico. It is the oil of chandan (sandalwood), coconut with fresh milk that anointed .their famous tresses. While the Indian Kaajal made from trifala, almond, camphor, cabbage and other precious herbs, all burnt in the oil of roses, was made famous by the Empress Nur Jehan, the Queen Consort of the Mughal Emperor Jehangir.

Today centuries later, the World Science Centre in New York has proved and accepted the incredible tonic effect of trifala, cabbage, rose, camphor and other precious herbs.

India's famous Moghul Queens used emerald, ruby and turquoise as eyeshadow, the powder of pearls to highlight under the eyebrows, a bark called missee to redden their lips and a concentrate of beetroot and sandalwood paste mixed with the oil of roses as rouge. The gold and silver dust that was used to spangle royal tresses has now been replaced by synthetic gold and silver hair sprays.

It might be of interest to know that not just synthetic cosmetics but all types of synthetic and man made fibers have a detrimental effect on health. For instance, it is known that women who wear nylon nighties, wake-up irritable while men who wear synthetic shirts to office are known to make rash and often wrong decisions because of the generation of static electricity which is absent in natural fibers. I would always recommend the use of natural spun fibers, be it cotton or silk.

Plastic combs have a similar effect, perhaps that is why in ancient times women, who used ivory or wooden combs were well-known for their serene temperaments.

I would, at this point, like to explode the myth of red, blue, yellow, pink and even green henna. There is no henna in these exicting colours. Just as there is no pink or mauve milk there is no multicoloured henna to be had, it is a ruse to cash in on the client's gullibility by using the word 'natural' when the henna they promote is nothing but synthetic. God has created only red henna... the rest of the colours are man-made. I disbelieve in the concept of 'synthetically created natural'. There can be and is only 'Natural'...pure extracts from the actual herbs.

There is no better way to health and beauty. Not just superficial, but that which radiates from within that is natural. I for one have always insisted that when the world had no synthetics, India always had her herbs. Also it is best to treat most of nature's ills with natural cures. I believe that India must and will lead the world cosmetic market in herbal beauty aids, because no matter how fast the West advances in cosmetic science, they cannot beat us at our centuries old herbal know-how and civilization.

Nature's Cosmetic Care: Natural Beauty Aids

THE concept of beauty itself has undergone one such transformation, that the change is found to be apparent in the field of modern cosmetic care. The emphasis has gradually shifted, from superficial treatments to a more positive approach that aims at protecting and preserving natural beauty, increasing attention is being paid to cosmetic ingredients and the methods that are followed in their use. This trend has been brought about by a growing awareness of the potential dangers that we are exposed to, which can actually mar the natural beauty. Among these are environmental pollutants, artificial heating and cooling, harsh treatments and the chemical substances contained in many cosmetic products. All these have a detrimental effect on beauty, as they cause damage to the health of the skin and hair. In other words, the further we go away from nature and natural living, the more we have suffered in terms of losing both health and beauty.

Today, the answer lies in turning back to Nature and to natural cosmetic care, through plant and herbal extracts. Treatments that were lost in the mist of time are being revived once more, to be viewed in the light of modern scientific techniques. It has been found that herbal beauty aids can be perfectly applied to the demands of modern cosmetology, both in terms of efficacy and safety.

Herbal remedies have survived through the ages because nature is a potent healer, with great restorative powers. Skin and hair care with these natural ingredients have also shown a complete lack of harmful side effects, irritative reactions and symptoms of intolerance. Chemical ingredients, on the other hand, also penetrate the skin and are absorbed by it, leading to a build-up of chemical residues in the system. This can lead to allergic reactions and other side effects. Many chemical substances used in cosmetic preparations are actually highly toxic. Therefore, the use of herbs is a way of ensuring safety from these harmful effects.

Treatments with plant extracts have also shown that the human body responds very well to natural substances, while it has an in-built resistance synthetic ingredients. Herbal and natural extracts contain valuable vitamins, minerals and enzymes, which are essential to the good health and beauty of the skin and hair. In fact, many biochemicals that exist in nature have not yet been identified and, therefore, cannot be reproduced synthetically. Apart from these various benefits, herbal beauty aids help to improve the functions of the skin and hair and thus enhance their beauty as a whole.

Indeed, Nature is not only an expert chemist, but the best cosmetologist. She has provided us with innumerable ingredients that have particular and versatile benefits in beauty care. In fact, we could even categorise them into terms that are familiar to us—like nourishers; cleansers, freshners, moisturisers, conditioners and so on. It would be quite appropriate to say that an entire range of cosmetic products exist in nature, to suit our individual requirements. Many of these are so common that we come across them daily in our kitchens and refrigerators. They are so versatile, that they not only help to beautify the skin and hair, but have preventive, protective and even corrective actions. Some have nourishing actions, while some are powerful cleansers. Some whip up the circulation and tone the skin, while other improve skin texture. The main advantage is that they help to achieve the perfect balances that are so essential to healthy skin and hair. What we have to do is to identify our individual needs and choose the appropriate products.

Cleaning is a routine that we all follow, but how many of us are aware of its importance to beauty? The ideal cleanser should not only remove wastes and impurities from the surface of the skin, but also protect it from damage and dehydration. Most soaps are alkaline in nature and remove the natural, protective, acid mantle of the skin. This leaves it predisposed to bacterial attacks and irritations. Soaps and harsh cleaners can also cause a depletion of both oil and mosture, making the skin dry and hastening the formation of lines and wrinkles. Herbal cleansers, on the other hand, have the ability to remove wastes and games, without disturbing the natural acid-alkaline balance of the skin and scalp. In fact, they even help to restore the desired balances.

Extracts of lemon, turmeric, cactus, aloe, ginseng have been found to be powerful natural cleansers. Products like yoghurt, egg white and papaya also cleanse effectively, apart from providing nourishment.

Some of these products contain enzymes which help to remove dead skin-cells from the skin surface and also prevent cellular build-up. Even potato extract is known to absorb impurities and cleanse the skin. Cactus and aloe have been combined with lemon to formulate an ideal rehydrant cleanser for dry and dehydrated skins. They cleanse the skin without causing a depletion of natural moisture.

Dry and ageing skins require emollients and regular moisturising to keep the texture soft and smooth. It is a combination of oil and moisture that keeps the skin supple and youthful. Many of us do follow a daily routine of skin nourishment, but we must pay attention to the products we use. Whatever we apply penetrates the skin, and the ingredients are, therefore, important. Herbal beauty aids contain properties what we are beneficial to the skin and also eliminate harmful effects. They also have therapeutic values and are a highly appropriate way of maintaining and restoring beauty to the skin.

Almond extracts have been used in both nourishing creams and masks, in combination with appropriate bases. Almond with a lanolin base, for instance, is ideal for the area around the eyes. Almond meal can be added to mask powders. Like almond, apricot is also nourishing for the skin. It contains Vitamin A, which heals scar tissue, eases out lines and restores elasticity to the skin. Vitamin oil, by itself is thick and sticky. Instead, plant products make the beauty routine easier and more pleasant. Natural ingredients have their own delicate fragrances too. A good nourishing cream, therefore, can be called a 'skin-food' cream, because it provides the nourishment, with which the skin can attain maximum health and beauty. Cabbage extract, carrot, wheat germ etc., have been combined to form natural skin-food creams.

Their rich mineral and vitamin contents have a rejuvenating effect. Natural ingredients like honey, milk, yoghurt and egg are valuable beauty aids. Eggs, for instance, contain lecithin, which is extremely nourishing, as also protein and phosphorous. Thus, these products supply the skin with the essential elements in their natural form. Normal, dry, dehydrated and mature skins all require daily nourishment with such skin-food creams.

The number of herbs that have been used in beauty treatments are so varied. Some have existed since ancient times as cosmetic items. Like extracts of rose, jamine and lavender. These, like others, have stood the test of time. They are ideal for oily and problem skins. Similarly, herbs like comfrey, camomile and sesame, when added to creams and lotions help to improve skin texture and colour. The combination of lemon and turmeric also helps to produce a more even colour tone and has been used to remove tans and pigmented patches. Herbal products are certainly much safer than the use of chemical bleaches. It is a lack of awareness that cause people to continue using chemical ingredients that not only hamper the normal functions of the skin, but cause irreparable damage. Careless applications of chemical bleaches can cause ugly burns, damage of healthy skin tissue and premature ageing.

The curative and soothing properties of herbal extracts are well known. Sandalwood, eucalyptus, clove, camphor, comfrey, arnica etc.

have antiseptic and germicidal actions yet, they help to heal and soothe inflammatory skin conditions and allergic rashes. Many of them have been formulated into cleansers, lotions and packs for oily skins and oily skin conditions, like pimples and acne. Sandalwood, for instance, is an ideal protection against the damaging effects of such excessive exposure and environmental pollution. Combined with a moisturising ingredient like honey, it can form an ideal barrier between the skin and environmental damage. Skin protection, after all, is an important aspect of beauty care.

HAIR CARE

The Structure of the Hair

A little elementary knowledge about the hair helps us to know just how to handle it. It also makes us aware of the damage that improper treatment can wrought.

Hair is a protein matter called 'keratin'. The hair that we see on the head is a horny substance that is actually 'dead'. It grows from a narrow tube below the surface of the scalp, which is called a follicle. At the base of the follicle is a small concentration of living cells called the papilla, which eventually form hair. Next to each follicle is a sebaceous gland which produces the natural oil that keeps the hair lubricated and shiny. Each hair is made up of three concentric layers. The outer layer has tiny, transparent scales which overlap each other and contribute to the shine. It is when these scales are removed that the hair loses its natural lustre and begins to look dull and rough. The middle layer contains the pigment that gives the hair its colour. There is also an inner layer, which may not be present if the hair is very fine.

Individual hair has three phases of development. The growth phase, the transition and the resting phase. At the end of the resting phase, the hair is shed and the same process is repeated by the hair that replaces it. This means that the hair on the head is at different stages of development—that is why it does not all fall out together. Hair fall, therefore, is natural. It is only when hair loss is more than replacement that thinning and balding sets in.

Hair, like the skin, owes its colour to melanin, the pigment that is formed in special cells. This depends mainly on hereditary characteristics and can also be influenced by racial factors. The texture of the hair also depends on these factors. Grey hair is a mixture of colourless hair and naturally coloured hair. When the pigment cells become inactive, the hair turns white. This can happen due to ageing or other reasons like illness, sudden shock or some internal disorder.

Hair has certain characteristics which helps us to know how to handle it. For one thing, hair is porous. This allows dyes and other lotions to penetrate the outer layer, causing the hair to be bleached, tinted or dyed. Permanent wave lotions also work in the same manner, by affecting the middle layer. Many chemical ingredients can damage the outer layer by lifting the scales, affecting both the texture and the look of the hair, which becomes dry, rough, brittle and lustreless. Hair also has elasticity. Styles and procedures which cause it to be stretched and pulled can damage it.

Hair may be dry or greasy, according to the activity of the oil producing glands. As the hair shaft grows, it gets coated with sebum, unless it can flow freely along the hair shaft. Dandruff and other scalp conditions can hinder growth. Under activity of the oil glands causes hair to dry, while over activity makes it greasy, attracting dirt and causing other problems.

Hair is fed by the blood flowing to the follicle. That is why, diet and a good blood circulation are so important. External care that we give helps to keep the scalp and hair in good condition. Thus, both internal health and external care are essential for healthy hair. Fatigue, mental tension and internal ill health are all reflected by the hair, as tension in the follicle muscles is affected.

Healthy, luxuriant hair is not difficult to achieve. Like all beauty assets, it needs constant care, with a basic knowledge of its particular characteristics. This knowledge should guide you in choosing the products that have been specially formulated for your kind of hair. Hair is like a beautiful, delicate fabric. Handle it that way.

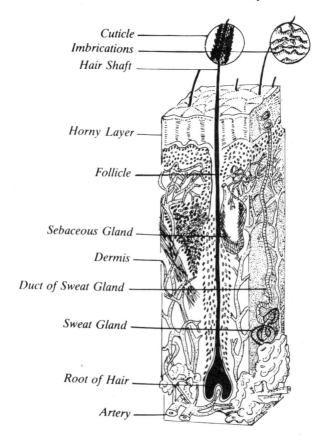

Cuticle
Imbrications
Hair Shaft
Horny Layer
Follicle
Sebaceous Gland
Dermis
Duct of Sweat Gland
Sweat Gland
Root of Hair
Artery

Hair Types

SHATONE SHANEL
SHALOCKS SHAOINT
SHAHAIR SHAMLA
SHALISMA

BEFORE you get down to hair care, it is important to first make sure what kind of hair you have, and then to look after it accordingly.

Dry hair, for example, would need plenty of nourishment. The roots, consequently, require extra oil and feeding. So, if you have dry hair, make it a point to use shampoos and tonics that have nutritive value, preferably with lanolin or vaseline bases. Egg shampoos go a long way towards preventing hair dryness.

Between hair sets, make use of a good hair conditioner. Hot oil treatments, like massages with warm olive oil are extremely beneficial for toning dry hair and for preventing it from becoming brittle. It is a good idea to steam the scalp before a hot oil massage by placing the head in front of the basin of steaming hot water, or soaking a towel in steaming water and then wrapping it around the scalp. This is an excellent method for opening up the pores of the scalp.

If hair is extremely dry, rub a little oil right into the roots before steaming. This proves even more beneficial and effective as subsequent steaming and a second massage with oil encourages better and deeper absorption. Since it is a simple treatment it can be easily done at home.

The main idea is to loosen and relax the scalp so that blood circulation in the head is accelerated, so that the sebaceous glands are stimulated.

For the right method of hair massage, a good nourishing hair preparation is required. The tips of the fingers are placed firmly on the head at the nape of the neck. With the fingers planted firmly on the head, work in small, circular strokes, first clockwise and then anti-clockwise, moving the skin of the scalp as you do so. A listless massage is useless.

Sometimes dryness of the scalp is due to nothing more than improper brushing. The brush bristles must be first pressed gently into the scalp, and then carried gently up to the hair tips. If the hair is brushed superficially, the oil glands become lazy because you are not exercising them sufficiently.

Wash hair with a lanolin based shampoo. Here is another beauty secret—always rinse your hair with a gentle acidic solution so as to rid the scalp of the alkaline mantle. This is easily and economically done by using two tablespoons of cosmetic vinegar in your last rinse. It helps prevent excessive oiliness and gives the scalp a chance to prevent as well as to rid itself of infection.

Oily Hair

SHATONE SHAHENNA SHAOINT
SHALOCKS SHANEL SHAHAIR

OILY hair requires a completely different therapy. It is important to remember that though brushing is very good for healthy hair, too much brushing is not good for oily hair because it stimulates oil glands that are already over-active. So, go easy on the brush. Get yourself a good tonic especially blended for your type of hair. You must take care to buy something that will brace the scalp and prevent oiliness.

If your hair is oily, it needs to be washed every third or fourth day or even more frequently, depending on your individual comfort. A good, nourishing liquid shampoo is often the best answer.

Excessive oiliness, when neglected, often leads to falling hair and premature baldness, especially in men, after 35. Treated in time, loss can be checked considerably, though, lost hair cannot be replaced.

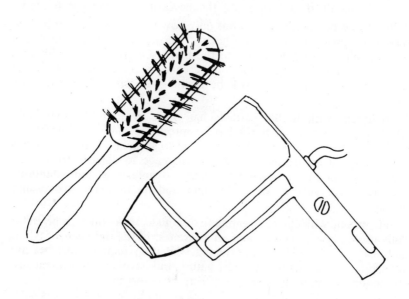

Dandruff is Dangerous

SHAOINT
SHATONE
SHANEL

THE hair, like the skin, is a barometer to the state of your internal health. If you are generally healthy and have a balanced diet, you will most probably find that your hair reflects it. On the other hand, illness, tension and deficiencies can affect hair and give rise to various problems. Hair is fed by blood flowing to the hair follicles, and this means that a good circulation is necessary for healthy hair. For this reason, the daily diet is of great importance and so are normal living habits. At some time or other, most of us are confronted with hair problems. One of the most common among these is dandruff, which can trigger off other problems like hair loss or acne.

Dandruff is a scalp disease. Some forms of dandruff can cause severe itching and when one scratches the scalp to relieve itching, further damage is caused. Any damage to the scalp with the nails can cause secondary bacterial infections. All these put together give rise to a more serious problem, accelerating hair loss and undermining the health of the hair. Dandruff as well as other bacterial and fungal infections of the scalp can be cured, but very often people get resigned to living with mild forms of dandruff and overlook the necessity of having it treated.

What one needs to know is not only how to cure it but also how to tackle the problem in all its aspects. The object is to restore health to the scalp, and by doing so, to the hair itself. If you bring about a change in your diet and living habits, consume more fresh foods and drink plenty of water, you will be tackling the problem at the grass roots.

Treatment with herbal extracts has been found to be extremely effective. A number of herbs have appropriate medicinal properties that can control infection. They also help to stimulate hair growth and are so mild in nature that there is no damage to delicate tresses. In fact, this is one factor which is a definite advantage, as many dandruff treatments are very harsh on the hair and finally leave it dry, and brittle.

Side by side with clinical treatments, a course of treatment is given for daily use, at home. This creates an awareness of the right way of taking daily care of hair. Herbs like henna, shikakai, reetha and amla are antiseptic ingredients provided by nature and have a wonderful cleansing action, without the harmful effects of detergents.

Light oil massage often helps to dislodge the dandruff flakes, though there is a myth about the effectiveness of head massage. In actuality, when there is hair loss, a vigorous massage can cause more hair to fall, as the roots are already weak. Besides, it can damage the hair shaft.

Hair is very delicate and should be handled very gently. The scalp should be massaged gently. The finger tips should be used to move the skin of the scalp in small circulatory movements.

For dandruff, a light massage with hot oil helps to rid the scalp of the flakes. Pure coconut oil or olive oil can be heated and applied on the scalp with a gentle massage at night. It should be left on overnight. Next morning the juice of one lemon should be applied an hour before shampooing. This can be a good weekly treatment for the scalp.

Henna is a natural product that also helps to control dandruff infections. However, one has to be very careful about the quality of henna that is used. Specially prepared henna powder, mixed with other ingredients, is effective in controlling dandruff and improving the texture of the hair.

Henna promotes hair growth, restores health and also conditions hair to a luxuriant, shiny, soft texture. It has an effective cleansing action, getting rid of toxic wastes that accumulates on the scalp, inhibiting natural hair growth.

These treatments help to create an 'acid mantle' on the scalp. The skin and scalp are normally acid and flourish in an acid medium.

Washing never harms the hair—It is the use of harsh shampoos that does. The hair should, in fact, be kept scrupulously clean, and this can be achieved by washing it at least twice a week. Hygiene is closely related to both health and beauty. Where dandrufff is concerned, there is a great necessity to keep the hair, combs, towels and pillow cases absolutely clean, as there are chances of re-infection.

Dandruff can be infectious and one should keep personal belongings separate, so that chances of infecting others are eliminated. Whenever you wash your hair, soak your brushes and combs in a mug of hot water containing an antiseptic solution. After washing hair, rinse it thoroughly, ending with a herbal hair rinse. Medicated rinses are available, which are actually anti-dandruff lotions, containing extracts of mint, brahmi, amla etc. so that the natural acid mantle is restored to the scalp.

What many do not know is that dandruff can cause skin problems like pimples, acne or rash. Those prone to dandruff often have spots and pimples on the forehead or cheeks and on the back. In fact it can lead to severe acne infections, spreading to the back, chest and upper arms, wherever the skin comes in contact with the hair.

Naturally healthy hair has that luxuriant and vibrant look that cannot be achieved by the best hairdressing efforts. No hairstyle however glamorous can work wonders, if the health of the hair is poor. Anything that is naturally beautiful has a 'look' that cannot be achieved by artificial means. The hair should have that vital, alive look with a shine, elasticity and bounce. It is this vitality that is responsible for the youthful quality that all women try so hard to achieve.

The Trauma of Hair Loss

SHATONE SHAOINT
SHAHAIR SHACARE

NOTHING alarms a person more than to be confronted with the problem of hair loss. Coming face to face with it can be a traumatic experience:.... one that can neither be shared nor happily camouflaged. Down the ages, ideals of beauty have placed a high value on the hair. Hair is never going to be out of fashion!

Hair loss can be triggered off by a variety of reasons and in many cases, the primary cause cannot be traced, making it difficult to achieve a cure by internal medication. In men, hereditary hair loss can progress to complete baldness, though it seldom affects women to such an extent. Yet, general thinning and falling of hair have become much more common among women. The cause may lie in the tension-ridden lives we lead. To compound the problem, our pattern of life is not so conducive to good health.

Internal diseases, reaction to drugs and dietary deficiencies are some common causes of hair loss. Among internal diseases, hormon or glandular disturbances account for many of the problems. Abnormal thyroid functioning, for instance, can be a cause. Women experience general thinning of the hair during certain stages of their lives, when hormonal changes occur. A heavy loss of hair occurs a few months after childbirth. Menopause and its accompanying hormonal imbalance can also cause it. Scalp diseases from bacterial or fungal infection can lead to hair loss.

A problem that is increasing is one of localized baldness, as opposed to general or diffused thinning of the hair. While hair growth may be normal in most areas, a few bald patches occur in many parts of the scalp. It may be confined to one area, or the patches may increase and enlarge, merging into each other and finally resulting in total baldness. This is known as alopecia areata. The causes of the disease are unknown and various factors have been attributed to it. One of these is emotional tension and anxiety. It is seen that anxiety increases the problem. In fact, emotional tension about the problem itself is almost always present.

Another cause of hair loss that is usually overlooked is hair damage. Excessive stretching and pulling, exposure to extreme heat for long periods, regular use of hair rollers have led to hair loss. Harsh treatments especially when the hair is pulled or stretched cause hair to break off in large numbers.

Each hair has a life span. When it falls off, it is replaced by another. When the rate of loss overtakes the rate of replacement, general thinning or hair loss occurs. It is, therefore, important to maintain the health of the hair to ensure that replacement does not suffer.

If there is a problem, it is essential to seek professional care, to determine the cause and treatment required. If scalp infection is the cause, it can be externally treated. Medicated hair tonics and ointments are prescribed to control infection and restore health to the hair. The problem of hair loss is checked and regrowth occurs. Clinical scalp treatments, to activate the follicles and increase blood circulation to the scalp, have helped. Cases of alopecia areata have also been clinically treated.

A large measure of success has been achieved through use of plant extracts that promote hair growth and improve the health of the scalp. Henna, shikakai, reetha, amla, bael and other extracts have been used in cases of acute hair loss. Not only do these extracts have therapeutic value, but the body responds well to natural organic products. Allergic reactions, or side-effects are non-existent.

It is essential to remember that hair must be treated very gently. When there is a problem of hair loss, hair becomes much more fragile than healthy hair. The use of brushes, or indiscriminate combing only aggravates the condition. Vigorous scalp massages are also taboo. It would only result in further hair loss. A wide-toothed comb should be used, only as much as is required to arrange the hair. The use of the brush should be stopped while the problem persists.

Alopecia aside, most cases of hair loss occur due to lack of care or hair damage, on the part of women themselves. Therefore, hair must be protected from treatments that cause damage, by following a routine. External care certainly helps in many cases. The means are at your disposal, in the form of specialized aids that promote the health of the scalp and the beauty of the hair. Unfortunately, most of us sit up only when we are confronted with a problem and then reach for the panic button!

Hair Dyeing   *SHAHAIR*

WHAT wrinkling is to skin, greying is to hair. Both are the signs that herald age. A woman despairs as much over the wrinkles that begin to line her face, as she does over the hair that turns white. This feeling of regret, for the youthful years that have passed is nothing new. In fact, the effort to retard the ageing process has existed since Eve. Beauty treatments, geared to delay or camouflage the signs of ageing, have been a major concern of the cosmetic world. Ageing, however, is a natural process. With time, the body ages and the signs of ageing manifest themselves in various ways... greying is one of them.

To understand the greying process, one must have a basic idea of the structure of the hair. The hair consists of concentric layers. The outermost layer is the cuticle, which is made up of tiny, transparent

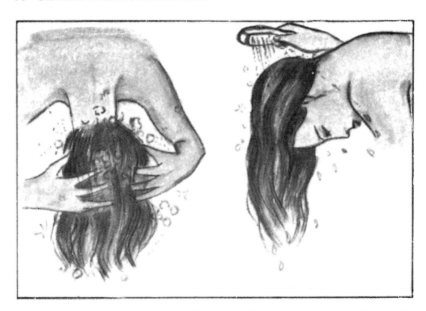

scales that overlap each other. The second layer is the cortex. It is in the cortex, just below the surface layer, that pigment, or colouring matter, forms. This gives the hair its colour. More the pigment, darker the colour of the hair will be. With age, pigment may not form, causing hair to be without colour or white. There may be other reasons why pigment may fail to form, but age is the most common factor.

The white strands mix with the dark ones and give the impression of grey hair. Naturally, when white strands appear, the question of how to deal with them causes much concern, not just from the aspect of concealing them, but also checking further greying. This question makes it important that few facts about the hair be known, so that damage to the hair is minimal.

To begin with, the strands that have already turned white cannot become black or dark again. The only way to change their colour is by dyeing. Dyeing, in fact, has become a common practice and a number of women resort to it. Unfortunately, most of them do not know the way the structure of the hair can be affected. Unless this is known, one is not able to take precautionary measures that help to control damage to the hair. Dyeing or colouring hair is not a modern beauty device. Women of ancient Rome and other civilisations were known to dye their hair, or even bleach them, using ingredients that often caused irreparable damage. Often, some of these treatments resulted in excessive hair loss. No wonder Ovid wrote: "Did I tell you to leave off dyeing your hair? Now you have none to dye!"

The chemical dyes and colourants that are in use today can also harm the texture and health of the hair. They contain ingredients that penetrate the cortex, resulting in damage to the texture. Regular dyeing, therefore, results in hair that is dry, brittle, rough and without lustre.

If hair damage is to be checked, it is essential to set up a protective care routine, as protection itself is one of the best preventive treatments. It has also been seen that regular care, started in good time, not only delays greying, but can also prevent it from spreading. These treatments include the use of products, containing natural hair darkening and protective agents, that have the added capacity of improving and maintaining the health of the hair.

Shampoo, rinses, tonics and conditioning powders, containing ingredients like henna, amla, shikakai, reetha and 'brahmi' have proved successful in maintaining the hair texture and health. These ingredients also have specific curative properties.

If the decision is made to dye hair with chemical dyes, it is all the more important to treat hair regularly with natural products, in order to protect the hair from harmful effects of chemicals and keep hair damage to the minimum. Dye your hair, if you must, but help to restore its beauty in terms of texture, quality and quantity.

One of the main advantages of using natural hair dyes and colourants is that they are completely safe and subject the hair and scalp to no hazards. Natural vegetable products are non-toxic and do not harm the structure of the hair. They do not destroy the outer layer or cuticle, as they do not enter the cortex. Henna is probably the best known natural colourant. It has the capacity of strengthening hair, as it coats the hair shafts. This not only protects hair, but gives it body and sheen. If there are only a few white strands which are visible there is no necessity to use chemical dyes. Henna can be used very effectively to conceal them.

Coffee or Kaththa (catechu) added to the henna paste gives hair a richer brown colour rather than a reddish tinge. The coloured strands blend with the rest of the dark hair and are well concealed. A question that is commonly asked is whether henna will colour the entire hair a flaming red. The answer to this is very simple. Dark hair will not catch a lighter colour and will not be coloured red. Henna will, in fact, add gloss and brighten dull hair.

Special henna powders, containing other valuable ingredients like amla and kohl are available. They have been used very successfully both as protective and preventive treatments, apart from curing many hair disorders. Regular applications of henna will, not only conceal but provide many other benefits. If there are a considerable number of strands that have already turned grey and you decide to dye them black, you should have a basic idea of the process that is involved.

Chemical dyes have a toxic base and have been known to cause irritations and allergies. The hairdresser will therefore do a patch test before dyeing your hair. This is usually done by applying the dye on a tiny area just behind the ear. A period of 24 hours must be allowed to see if any skin irritations or allergies are caused. If not, the dye may be used. It is better to have the hair dyed by a hairdresser, as there are particular instructions that must be followed regarding the lotions used and great care must be taken. No attempt should be made to dye eyebrows or eyelashes with these dyes.

Fine hair can be dyed easily as it absorbs better, while coarse hair is more resistant to colour. This itself would require the use of more and more quantities of the dyeing lotion as time goes on, since dyeing makes hair coarse, with repeated applications.

As far as the daily routine is concerned, the hair should be washed with a very mild shampoo, so as not to subject it to harsh detergents. An amla shampoo is ideal, as it lubricates dry hair and has a powerful cleansing action without disturbing the oil moisture balance. It also restores the acid-alkaline balance of the scalp. Amla keeps the hair soft and shiny and checks further greying. The harsh ingredients in chemical dyes remove natural oil and moisture, leaving both the hair and scalp very dry. A hair rinse, used with shampoo, completes the hair washing procedure and leaves hair in a manageable condition. Regular conditioning treatments with henna improves both the look and the general health of the hair. Thus hair that is dyed requires special care, so that the damage may be reversed to a great extent.

One of the most important aspects of beauty is to be aware of the detrimental effects of various treatments. Some treatments can have disastrous results, involving a great deal of time, effort and expense to gain what is lost. In some cases, damage may be permanent. As far as possible, avoid treatments that expose the hair and skin to harm. For instance, when you feel you must resort to such methods, be sure to supplement them with an appropriate routine of daily care, so that the natural beauty of such valuable assets may be preserved as long as possible.

Tips on Hair Conditioning

SHACARE
SHAHAIR

HEALTHY hair is one that is shiny, with resilience and elasticity neither too limp nor too dry. Hair that is dry will have the fly-away look and acquire split ends easily. It will be dull and without lustre. In other words, healthy hair is one which is balanced, with the sebaceous glands producing the right amount of oil to keep it glossy. The texture of healthy hair is smooth, with body and bounce. The delicate balance can be upset very easily due to various reasons. Among these, lack of care and harsh treatments are probably the most common. Treatments like perming, straightening and dyeing as well as harsh shampoos can remove the natural acid mantle of the scalp, leaving an alkaline residue. This can affect the hair's natural elasticity, making it dry and brittle.

Conditioning is a way of giving the hair a more intense kind of nourishing treatment. It helps to protect the hair by counteracting dryness, making it smooth and easier to manage. Herbal lore is replete with age old conditioning treatments, some of which are followed even today.

Tea and beer rinses are also known to improve the look of the hair. Used tea leaves should be boiled again in enough water. Strain the liquid, cool and use as a rinse after your shampoo. Beer is said to give the hair body and make it manageable.

Lemon juice, added to a mug of water and used as a last rinse helps oily hair, while honey-water helps to moisturise a dry scalp.

One age-old recipe suggests that 40 to 50 drops of honey should be added to a pint of water to make this honey lotion.

Among the best known conditioners is henna. It is an extremely versatile product and benefits all kinds of hair. A henna paste mixed with other ingredients leaves hair supple, shinning and easy to handle.

Henna can be mixed with yoghurt, lemon juice, egg and coffee. If the hair is dry, add a teaspoon full of pure coconut or olive oil. The paste is applied on the head and washed off after about 45 minutes to an hour. Henna helps to cleanse the scalp and remove impurities and wastes, thus improving the normal functions of scalp. It is also an intensive nourishing treatment and helps to strengthen hair. Hair texture becomes smooth and silky and acquires a shine. The hair not only appears thicker, but becomes more resilient.

Due to its versatility, henna has proved to be one of the best treatments for hair problems. Henna has been mixed with other valuable ingredients like amla, kohl, brahmi and arnica into a conditioning powder, to restore health and beauty to hair. It helps to stimulate hair growth and control various scalp disorders. Dandruff and other seborrhoeic conditions have been treated successfully by conditioning with this herbal powder.

The key to beautiful hair is a healthy scalp. If it is kept clean of accumulated glandular wastes and dirt, if the normal balances are maintained, it will perform its functions well. Therefore, appropriate treatments must be given to the hair regularly to maintain its texture, health and beauty.

Hair care is very simple once you know what the requirements are and can relate them to appropriate products. It also entails an awareness of what can be wrought by harsh treatments and wrong products. Each hair is made up of very delicate fibre that must be protected if its beauty is to be maintained. It is up to you to ensure that it is always kept in top condition.

Herbs for Hair

FROM organic foods to herb based cosmetics, the cycle has turned a full circle, back to nature. Synthetic shampoos are now accused of causing several irritations, including dandruff and excessive dryness of hair and scalp. Now the natural goodness and purity of nature's gift to beautify hair and skin have been rediscovered. More and more women, all over the world are realising the real worth of natural herbs for cosmetic purpose. Vegetable dyes and rinses were already known in ancient times. But these have come back into fashion in the past two years. Synthetic conditioners, tints, rinses and dyes deprive the scalp of nature oils and proteins.

Herbs are being used to bring life to dull hair, to colour grey hair, and to bring a change in the original colour of the hair and also to clean it.

Rinses like Camomile tea is claimed to give a golden tint to hair, while Chinese tea is supposed to brighten dark hair.

Dyes: Herbs like henna, walnut bark, indigo, which were used even in the ancient times when women first started being conscious of beautifying their hair and skin are still in practice.

Indigo: Gives a blue colour to the hair. It is mixed with henna to make what is called the Persian dye, still widely used in the East. The colour obtained varies according to the proportion of the two ingredients. It must be left on the hair for several hours for the dye to be effective.

Walnut Bark: Gives an attractive brown colour to the hair. **Henna** is the Persian name for a small shrub. A paste made of powdered henna leaves is of ancient repute as a cosmetic. It has been used by Egyptian and Indian women to dye their finger nails and make intricate patterns on their hands and feet in an orange red colour, which was considered to add to their beauty.

It was and is still used for dyeing hair and beards, as well as horses' manes. Moreover, distilled water from the flowers is used as perfume too.

Henna is used by beauticians to get a bright red colour or a burnished copper, or just to get highlights. Henna gives a coppery bronze or reddish effect. Mixed with coffee seeds, the hair assumes a rich brown colour.

Henna when used on grey hair gives a carroty red colour; used on dark hair, it gives a rich auburn tone. Henna is usually applied on strands of clean, shampooed hair while it is still damp and is left on the hair for an hour or so.

Hair, your crowning glory, needs thorough cleansing and gentle care. Synthetic shampoos have been accused of leaving the hair "squeaky"— which means they wash off the natural oils from the hair. Herbs like reetha, shikakai, amla have retained their popularity and are used by many to keep hair clean. But to overcome the messy, tedious process of using these herbs, a new brand of herbal shampoos have been introduced. These herbal shampoos claim to be 93 per cent pure, made from herbs procured in India and abroad. These are obtained in four different varieties, to suit four kinds of hair, namely Orange Blossom for oily hair, Camomile for dry hair, Wild Cherry for normal hair and Rosemary for dandruff. The shampoos are made from the softest water and pure extract of fresh cured herbs in a floral, oily and cherry base.

CARING FOR THE EYES

THE eyes are, probably, the most wonderful part of the anatomy. They present us with such a variety of sights, and that too in exact dimensions of space and vision. Even where beauty is concerned, most people rate the eyes as the most important feature of the face. For one thing, the eyes get the most attention. When people talk to you, they look at your eyes. The eyes are called "the mirrors of the soul" and rightly so, because they express the exact emotions that we feel. They can convey anger, disappointment, sorrow, and joy more effectively than words.

The eyes are really most revealing. Not only do they reflect our feelings, but truthfully record the passing years, the state of our health, the care we give them and, naturally, also the neglect and abuse that we subject them to. In fact, the first signs of ageing begin to manifest themselves on the skin around the eyes. No matter how expert the make-up, any sign of ill-health, fatigue, or lack of care does show through.

The skin around the eyes is extremely vulnerable. It is thin in texture and lines and wrinkles very easily. There are no sebaceous (oil-producing) glands in this region, that keep the skin soft and smooth. Therefore, it is very important to know the exact treatment that eyes require.

As important as external treatment, it is necessary to take a look at your habits.....the kind

of food you eat, the work you do, the amount of sleep you have. The eyes are the most over-worked features of the face. They can be strained by reading for long periods, or by watching too much television. Harsh lights, wind, dust, emotional anxieties, excess of alcohol and smoking can all be detrimental. Many of us spend long hours doing close work....intense reading, bending over files and figures. The result of so much strain tells on the eye muscles, which become tense and weary, leading to problems related to vision and appearance.

The eyes reflect the state of internal health to such an extent that, sometimes, ophthalmologists can even detect the presence of certain diseases, even before subsequent tests confirm them. The eyes can, thus, warn you, about the possibility of an internal disease. Any problem of vision, however minor, should be referred to the doctor immediately. Similarly, other conditions, like redness, watering, flashes of light, presence of black dots, excessive sensitivity to light, or pain need professional advice and medical examinations.

Healthy eyes are clear. The white is really white and the pupils are bright, with smooth skin on the eyelids and around. Excessive smoking, and even working in a smoky atmosphere for long periods can strain the white of the eyes and make them dull and yellowish. Illness or dietary deficiencies can rob eyes of their sparkle. Fatigue and insomnia give the eyes a tired look that can add years to a face.

Sleep is one of the most important factors for eye beauty. Without adequate sleep, the eyes can look puffy, blood shot and even become encircled by dark shadows. At least seven hours of sleep is the average daily pattern. Whenever you miss out on sleep, catch up on it as soon as you can. As and when time permits, take a few minutes off to just close the eyes and relax.

Daily diet is equally important. Adequate Vitamin A is required for healthy bright eyes. It is found in liver, egg yolk, fish, butter, milk, yellow and leafy green vegetables. Carrots, for instance, are particularly rich in Vitamin A. Your daily diet must include fresh fruits and vegetables, so that you get a variety of the other nutrients. Your fluid intake should be adequate. Drink at least 6 to 8 glasses of water daily, with fresh fruit juices. This is all the more essential if your eyes have the tendency to puffiness.

When it comes to taking care of the skin around the eyes, it is essential to choose products carefully. Even make-up can often cause allergic reactions. If there is any itching, redness or soreness, discontinue the use of all cosmetics and consult your doctor. It is foolish to compromise on quality when you select your cosmetic products.

The skin around the eyes requires very gentle handling. Cream should be applied gently, without any massage. Massage on this region needs a professional touch and should never be done by inexpert hands. Any pulling or stretching of the skin can cause damage to the delicate tissues. Use a very light touch to apply creams, or remove make-up. Choose cleansers and nourishing creams that are particularly suited to the care of the skin around the eyes—like a light moisturised cleanser and an almond-based cream. Heavy creams should not be applied and no creams, or cosmetics, should be left on overnight. Avoid the skin around the eyes when you apply face masks. Only those that are especially meant for eye care should be used.

Your daily care routine should consist of cleansing, using moist cotton wool and a moisturised cleansing gel, wiping gently to remove all make-up. Soap and water are not adequate for removing all make-up debris, apart from causing the skin to become too dry. Harsh astringent lotions are taboo for this area. After cleansing, apply an almond-based under-eye cream and remove after ten minutes, again using moist cotton wool. Almonds not only nourish the skin, but have a gentle bleaching effect, maintaining the colour tone of the skin. Regular care is essential to keep the skin soft, moist and youthful. Therapy with cactus aloe cleansers and almond under-eye creams have helped to revitalise and rejuvenate the skin around the eyes.

Tired eyes can be soothed with eye-pads, containing extracts of suitable ingredients. A rose-based skin tonic can be used. Keep a small bowl with the tonic in the refrigerator. Dip cotton wool pads in this chilled liquid and use them as eye pads. Lie down and relax for at least ten minutes, while you have them on. Cucumber juice, or cucumber slices also benefit skin around the eyes. Potato extract reduces puffiness and has a mild astringent effect on the skin. These treatments help to remove the fatigued look and add brightness to the eyes.

Keep your eyes protected from long exposure to strong sunlight. It is the glare created by sunlight that can harm the eyes. It is a good idea to wear sunglasses out doors, but make sure of the quality of the glass used.

There are a few exercises that help to relax the eyes. One such is 'palming' or 'cupping' the eyes. Put the base of your palm over closed eyes and press gently. Cover the eyes with 'cupped' palms. Open the eyes and look into the darkness created by your palms. Both these are very relaxing. While doing close reading work, close your eyes for a few seconds, from time to time. This will protect them from strain. Even blinking helps the eyes. When we blink, the eyes are bathed by moisture and cleansed. Rest is the best relief for tired eyes.

You can try a few exercises to relieve muscular tension and maintain the health of the eyes.

1. First look at a very close object in front of you and then switch over to an object as distant as possible. This can be done by facing a window, so that the eyes command a sweeping view.

2. Standing in one place, rotate the eyes, without moving the head, in a complete circle, first clockwise and then anti-clockwise.

3. With the head erect, move the eyes—first looking at the roof and then the floor. Repeat this ten times. Again, look first to the extreme right ·and then to the extreme left. While doing these exercises, remember not to squint when you move the eyes. In between the exercises, relax your eyes by closing them tightly and then opening them wide. In fact, this can be most relaxing whenever the eyes feel fatigued.

Last, but not the least, breathe.....really breathe. We live such tension-ridden lives that our muscles need relaxation. Even the eyes suffer from want of oxygen and breathing deeply will supply it to them. The pattern of life that we lead imposes a great deal of strain on our eyes. So, we must try consciously to help them to relax. It does not matter what shape they have. Healthy, bright, sparkling eyes are beautiful.

HINTS FOR PRETTY HANDS

WHAT we tend to forget is that our hands are on display all the time. Even when we talk, we use gestures and gesticulations!

Rough, wrinkled hands and chipped nails can really shatter the entire illusion. The condition of the hands depends on the care you give them... and this is so true of every aspect of the appearance. Good grooming includes pretty hands.

The hand is really a marvel. It has 28 bones, including the wrist, all wonderfully balanced. No wonder it has so much mobility and expression. In fact, the hands can speak a language of their own.

On the back of the hands, the skin is soft and thin. It is prone to early wrinkling. On the palm, the skin is thick and tough. The palm has no sebaceous glands, like most other parts of the body have. Therefore, it has no natural lubrication and can become exceedingly dry and rough. The skin chaps easily. The use of detergents compounds the problem, giving you a pair of hands that you wish you could hide. The hands also show up age quicker than most parts of the body. So prevention through daily care is the only answer.

After your bath, or any washing chore, always massage your hands with a lubricating cream. A lemon turmeric cream is ideal. Lemon cleanses while turmeric softens the skin. The combination is protection against chlorine and detergent damage.

SHAPEACH
SHAPEEL
SHAHANDS
SHAGLOSS

Every night, before bedtime, use a cream on the hands, massaging for a few minutes. Apricot hand creams are excellent for providing nourishment to the skin. Additionally, apricot helps to tighten the skin and prevent wrinkles.

For an emergency treatment for coarse, rough skin, apply the cream lavishly at bedtime and go to sleep with cotton gloves on. Almond cream with a lanolin base is also good for the hands, giving them a mild bleaching treatment and nourishing the skin at the same time.

If you can afford the luxury of time, apply a bit of your daily face mask to your hands. This helps to cleanse, tone and smoothen the skin. At least, give them this treatment once a week.

Specially formulated body packs are also available that can be used on the hands.

Exercising the hands helps to make them flexible and improve circulation. Try the following exercises, repeating them six to ten times.

1. Clench your fists tightly for a second and then throw open the fingers as wide as posssible.

2. Put your hands out in front of you, palm, down. Press the

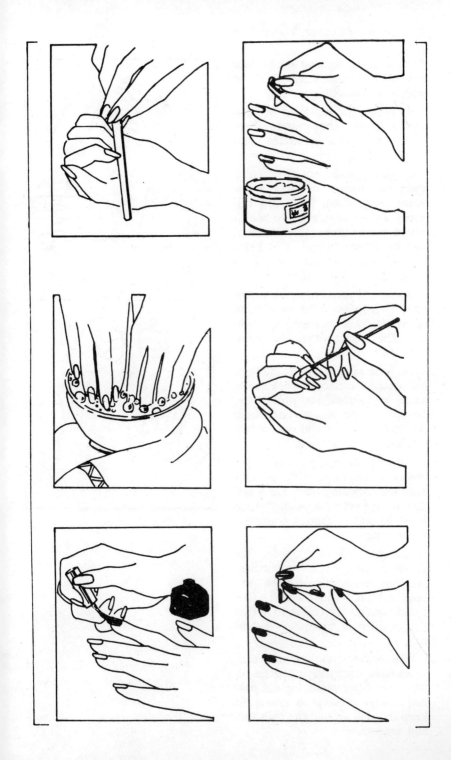

fingers tightly against each other and then thrust them apart as widely as possible.

3. Allow the hands to be limp and relaxed. Then rotate them from the wrists in circles, first clockwise and then anti-clockwise.

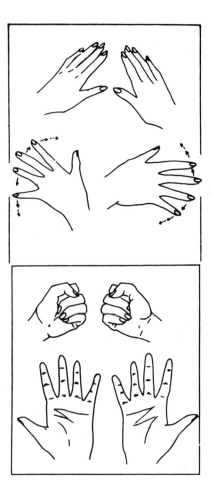

If your hands are tired, give them an instant reviving treatment. Soak them for a few minutes in warm water, to which about two to three tablespoons of salt have been added. This helps to soothe them and get rid of waste debris and scales.

Another treatment which stimulates circulation is to soak them alternatively in hot and cold water. This also soothes the nerve endings.

A professional hand massage and manicure once a week really helps to maintain and protect the beauty of the hands. For home manicures, you would need a few implements to aid you.

Among the essential ones are emery boards for shaping the nails and smoothening the hardened skin on the sides. A pumice stone helps to soften callouses and remove stains.

Orange sticks are needed for gently pushing back the cuticles. Acetone and nail varnish are required if you would like to add colour. A cream to soften the cuticles is absolutely essential.

Nail polish removers and acetones have a very drying effect on the skin. After removing old polish, always massage a cream to keep the skin around the nails soft and smooth.

HINTS FOR HAPPY FEET

MANY of us neglect our feet, usually thinking that they are hidden from public view. But foot care is very important, not only for the appearance, but also for health. The feet, after all, hold up the entire body and we expect a lot from them. We make them carry our weight in all kinds of footwear, over all sorts of surfaces. Happy feet certainly make you feel better—and like every other part of the body, respond wonderfully well to regular care.

Problem feet can arise from many reasons—ill-fitting shoes, poor posture or heredity. Daily care, with regular exercise, can really help to overcome most of these.

Good foot posture does help to put the entire body into balance. When you stand or walk, the toes should point almost straight ahead. Lift the arches of the feet slightly so that your body weight is supported by the outside edges of the soles of your feet. Overweight people put excessive strain on the arches, resulting in aching feet and backaches.

The best exercise for the feet is walking barefoot, on grass if you can. Good alternative exercises can also be followed. Stand up straight feet, pointed, ahead, rise up on the toes and then lower yourself. This strengthens the arches of the feet. Curling the toes, as if you are trying to pick something off the floor with your feet, also help to strengthen the metatarsal arch and prevents callouses.

SHACREAM
SHAFAIR

Corns and callouses are caused by ill-fitting shoes that rub the skin or squeeze the feet. Shoes should not be too tight, as constant pressure over bony areas interferes with the circulation of blood, leading to corns.

During the summer months, avoid closed shoes. Open sandals are much better. Properly fitted shoes are essential for relief from foot pain. Those who walk a lot or stand for long hours, need shoes with thick soles and low heels.

The front should be wide enough to allow enough space for the toes. During the hot and wet season, feet can pick up infections. Athlete's foot is one that is caused by fungus that thrives on wet, soggy, skin.

Wear sandals for maximum ventilation and keep the skin as dry as possible. Expose your feet to the air as often as you can.

Ingrowing toe nails can also cause a great deal of discomfort. The nails should be cut squarely across. Ingrowing toe nails should not be rounded as they would tend to grow into the flesh even more.

Clean, well-kept nails lend the entire foot class and dignity that are most essential for perfect grooming. Soaking feet in warm soapy water helps to soften the nails, which can be cut or filed more easily.

Do not cut the cuticles of the toe

nails, as the cuticles help to protect them. They should be creamed and pushed back very gently.

A good foot massage is a real pleasure. A weekly pedicure would normally include a foot massage, and most beauty parlours provide it. The rotating, kneading motion, adopted by the masseur is most relaxing for the feet and also keeps the skin in good condition.

Cleanliness is, of course, a must. Dirt and stale sweat secretions must be removed by scrubbing feet daily with soap and water. Rub heels with a pumice stone to get rid of dead skin and clean nails with a brush.

Creaming feet daily goes a long way towards keeping the skin soft and adds to foot beauty.

Most foot problems benefit from alternating hot and cold baths. This helps to improve circulation and relieve · pain. The feet, very often, suffer from poor blood circulation.

Take two buckets. Fill one with hot water and the other with cold water. The water should be enough to reach the calves. Place your feet in hot water first, for a few minutes and then in cold water for a few minutes.

Repeat this at least five times, starting and ending with hot water. Dry the feet thoroughly and then massage with cream. An apricot cream is ideal for the feet.

Stretch the toes and move the front part of each foot in a circular motion. Contrast baths, followed

by massage and exercise, provide instant relief for tired, aching feet.

Happy feet will make you happier.

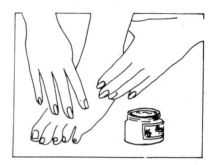

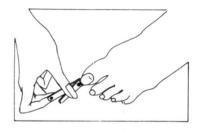

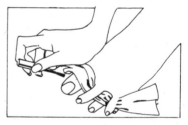

OF NEGLECTED NECKS AND BACKS

Neck

A long, graceful neck has always been considered a symbol of beauty. It is also one of the areas which begins to show the tell-tale signs of age first.

Unfortunately, it is a portion of the anatomy that is sadly neglected. Yet the neck is always in evidence and certainly requires a lot more attention than it gets. Faces may be regularly cleansed and beautifully made up, but the neglected neck provides a terrible contrast.

It is one of the areas which is most vulnerable to ageing lines and unbecoming folds that cannot be disguised even by the most expert make up techniques. Needless to say, daily nourishment and care is as important as the daily attention that is given to the face.

Always remember to hold your head up, as it is good for the neck and for general postures. Models practise walking with a book balanced on the head. It not only improves the walk, but helps to prevent double-chins. Sleeping without a pillow is another way of battling this bulge!

If you are above the age of 25, you could start taking regular facials. A facial massage includes the neck and helps to keep lines at bay. For your daily routine, allot a minute or two to the neck, preferably before your bath.

Using a pre-bath gel, massage the neck area with downward strokes, one hand following the other. A gel containing lemon and turmeric provides a gentle whitening effect.

Very often the colour of the skin on the neck is darker than that of the facial skin. The lemon-turmeric gel would eliminate this colour difference. The skin will be kept well moisturised and thus counteract the harsh, drying effect of soap.

Remember to do what most people forget when they apply facial masks—apply it on the neck too. For older skins, there are professional remedies. A range of highly specialised masks are being used to reduce such problems to a most appreciable extent.

Never neglect the neck... not unless you wish to sport Victorian fashions of ruffles, high collars and scarves and say farewell to low necklines and swimsuits. A smooth, willowy neck will always be 'in'. Make daily care a habit and you will soon find caring for the neck is not really such a pain in the neck!

Back

SHADEW SHAMASK II
SHAHERB SHABATH

THE back is another trouble spot that owes its troubles to neglect. Not having eyes at the back of the head, we end up with backs that are cases of "out of sight, out of mind". Yet it is very much a part of us and gets enough attention...but, from others.

We moan at the sight of one spot on the face and happily go around with backs laden with pimples, lumps and scars. Its high time we turned around and had a look at the back.

This area is very rich in oil glands and that is one reason why one rarely gets wrinkles on the back. But alas, it makes the skin prone to blackheads, which, as you may know, sets the stage for pimples, acne and spots. The result is a discoloured skin and scars when these blemishes have healed.

We tend to neglect the problem just because it involves a portion of the anatomy that we cannot see. Neglect causes the infection to spread rapidly and before we know it, the skin is a mass of pimples. If there is dandruff, a rashy or pimpled back is very common.

A great deal of attention should be paid to the back while bathing. Use a long handled soft brush, or a cloth to scrub the area gently to keep it clean and free of clogged pores. If there are pimples, use an anti-pimple lotion to check the infection.

For scars, or for a discoloured skin, the lemon-turmeric gel can be applied on the area, while an anti-blemish ointment should be rubbed into the skin before bedtime. In case there is dandruff, get it treated as well, or else you will keep reinfecting yourself.

The skin on the back is usually exposed, especially during summer. It is not only subject to view, but also to elemental effects, of which the sun plays the most havoc. It tans the skin, making it dry and flaky.

The object is to keep the skin soft, smooth and well-moisturised, whether it happens to cover your face or your back. Always remember that it is a part of YOU. Your skin, regardless of the part it covers, deserves to be kept well-nourished, toned, alive and clean.

Whether it is your back or your neck, it has every right to look as good as your face!

MAKE-UP AS AN ART

THE expertise with which make up is applied is called an art. The dictionary describes the word 'art' as 'skill'—especially applied to representation, design or imaginative creation. This definition is so apt. Make-up is a technique that actually creates the look that one wishes to project. It is the outcome of a great deal of experiment and practice, trial and error. It is not a natural talent, but a technique that is learnt and mastered, bringing into use one's power of observation, good taste and colour sense.

One can go wrong so easily—as is evident in the way so many attractive faces are hidden behind masks of heavy foundation and layers of paint. The entire result is self-defeating as the attention of the beholder goes to the make-up rather than the wearer!

When you first begin applying make-up, it is best to observe discretion. Begin by choosing all cosmetics with care and keep your individual skin tone and texture in view.

Unless you learn to suit your make-up to individual needs, demands of time of day and occasion, you will actually be ignoring the basic principle. Your make-up will have no relation to the face you are supposed to be enhancing.

Expertise comes only through acquiring skill in the use of all the equipment that is available, so that you can create the look you want, toning down defects and emphasizing attractive features. Only through experiments with colours and shades can you learn the techniques and pick up tips that help to enhance beauty. Expertise and skill allows creativity, so that colours can be mixed to produce the effect that compliments the skin tone as well as the clothes you are to wear.

Professional make-up is based on three fundamental techniques-blending, shadowing and highlighting. Blending takes into consideration the different steps that are followed, from preparing the skin, applying foundation, adding colour, to putting the finishing touches. Each step is separate, but the entire effect is 'total' that does not make the steps obvious. This can only come with very careful blending. No separations and demarcations should be visible. Each cosmetic that is used, should be blended carefully with the next one. For instance, when you add colour with rouge or blush-on, it should not stand out as a separate area of colour.

Similarly, foundation should not give the face a mask-like effect. It should blend with the skin tone and no lines of difference should be apparent at the jawline or throat.

The area around the eyes should also blend with the rest of the face. The skin around the eyes shows up tiny lines and wrinkles very easily and requires a very thin layer of foundation, applied with a light touch, and yet blending in with the face.

Select the colours with great care and experiment first. You may find that mixing two shades will produce the right colour for you. To know the exact proportions in which colours are to be mixed, you have to try them on your skin. Make-up should be applied with a light touch, stroking outwards.

Shadowing requires even more skill. In fact, it is an art in itself. Make-up artists learn to use this skill for different kinds of lighting and to suit different purposes.

For instance, make-up for the television screen would differ from make-up for the films. Similarly, you have to keep in mind the kind of lighting you will be exposed to. At night, under artificial lights, make-up must be brighter. Under neon-lighting, colours with blackish and bluish undertones should be avoided. For instance, a dark maroon lipstick will drain the face of colour by looking almost black.

Shadowing is not to be confused with eyes-shadow! Professional make-up artists use shadowing to correct facial flaws. They can actually change the shape of a particular feature so that it blends better with the rest of the face, creating an illusion of better balance. Shadowing tricks are done with colours that are slightly darker than the main shade of base. The principle behind shadowing is that a darker colour de-emphasizes or 'tones down'. For instance, a wide jawline can be slimmed down by blending the shadow from under the cheekbones towards the corners of the mouth and then back towards the jawbone. The darker shade of the shadow thus helps to narrow down the jawline.

Shadowing is based on observation. One must first study the features very well to know the exact flaws and the shape that would help to create a better balance and thus enhance the beauty of the face. The idea is to re-contour the face.

The darker colour that you use for shadowing should blend well with the main shade. Again, this should not stand out as a separate area of colour.

Thus, through skilful shadowing, a broad forehead can look narrower, a double chin can be slimmed down, while round chubby cheeks can acquire an illusion of exotic cheek hollows.

It is obvious that shadowing is a technique that cannot be mastered overnight. It requires a great deal of practice and extreme patience.

While dark colours de-emphasizes, lighter colours give emphasis. They highlight a particular area or feature, and bring it forward. Both shadowing and highlighting are techniques that compliment each other. While the dark colour tones down an area, it brings forward the rest of the areas. These can be further emphasized or brought forward by using a lighter shade and will, in turn, compliment the shadowed area by making it recede further.

For instance, the cheekbones can be highlighted with a lighter colour when they are flat, thus adding to them. Consequently the impression of cheek hollows are created lower down. This gives the face a more contoured effect.

So, actually, three different shades of colour are being used, though belonging to the same tone. There is the main base or foundation, a lighter colour to emphasize and a darker colour to shadow. All these colours must be blended well with each other, as well as with the colour tone of the skin. Just choosing the right colours is itself a major step.

Using these techniques, it is possible to reconstruct a particular feature of the face. A nose that is too wide, for instance, can look narrower by using the highlighting light colour down the centre of the nose in a straight line. Next, the darker colour is brushed along the sides of nose. The two colours are then blended together so that no lines of difference are visible.

Similarly, the dark colour is used to tone down cheeks that are too round, creating a more exotic look with higher cheek bones and cheek hollows in the right place. The entire idea is to create a perfect balance.

Professional make-up techniques are, therefore, based on creating visual illusions. The skill is used to produce an effect that is natural. This, in fact, is the essence of good make-up so that the mind believes what the eyes see.

Make-up should be subtle, regardless of the time, effort and equipment that may have been used. Whatever the technique, remember that your make-up should be in keeping with your face and personality, bringing forward the best features of your face in the most natural way. The eventual effect should be one that highlights the fundamental beauty of your face.

Optical Illusion

SHALIPS SHASHINE
SHAROUGE SHABRIDE
SHAEYES SHALINE
SHADUST

IN order to be beautiful, a woman must have the will to be beautiful. Make-up can prove the determined woman's greatest ally, provided she uses it subtly and skilfully; misused it can have disastrous effects.

Make-up falls into two simple categories; (a) simple make-up (b) illusion make-up. In this chapter we will deal with the latter.

Remember that the perfect face is oval. Any facial cut deviating from this must be made to look oval. In order to decide what shape your face is, mentally divide it into three equal parts—first, the forehead from the hairline to the eyebrows; second from eyebrows to the base of the nose; and third from the base of the nose to the tip of the chin. These proportions, within a perfect oval, constitute the measurements of a classically beautiful face.

But most faces are not oval. This is where the art of illusion make-up comes in. Make-up can be applied so skilfully that it gives an oval look to a face of any shape. Once you have determined your facial shape go ahead with the problem systematically.

Subject—you.

Object—To create an illusion or impression of beauty; to play up your best features and play down the weaker ones.

Study carefully, by wrapping a scarf around your head, the shape of your individual features, one by one. Then consider your face as a whole.

Applied skilfully, illusion make-up can give the impression of symmetry, and it can play down facial faults. If the shape of your face is not to your liking, it is a good idea to learn how to use two shades of foundation in order to create the illusion you desire.

Keeping in mind the fact that dark colour recedes and light colour projects, darker foundation should be applied along the cheek, at the fullest part, to slim down a moon face. A brighter shade will emphasize features that are too small.

A square or rectangular face will require dark foundation to shade the lower jaw line in a diagonal line from the ear to the tip of the chin. Likewise, shading on the upper corners of the forehead should be used to correct a heart shaped face.

The size and shape of the mouth can also be improved by lipstick, lipbrush and a little skill. Whenever you use a lipstick, first clean the lips thoroughly and then cover them with the same foundation that you have used on the rest of the face. If you have a lip pencil, outline the shape of the lips you would like to have—smaller, fuller or prettier than the ones you already have. Fill the lip colour in carefully the way an artist paints in colours.

For a protruding lip, whether it is the upper or lower one, use a slightly darker lipstick on that lip to make it look smaller. Use a lighter shade of lipstick on the finer lip. Very full lips should be outlined just inside the natural line. Very fine lips can be made to look fuller by drawing the lip line in a lighter shade of lipstick outside the natural one.

To make that special pleasant expression, bring the corners of the lips a little higher than the corners of the mouth, and as you fill in the lipstick, make the colour meet this point at the corners. If you wish to make the finer lips look the same size as the protruding one, use on it a lipstick one shade lighter.

The eye liner should start from the centre of the upper lid for normal eyes.

For eyes that are set too wide apart, the eye liner should start from the innermost corner of the eye, working gently outwards.

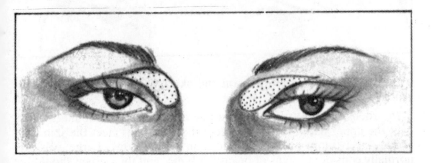

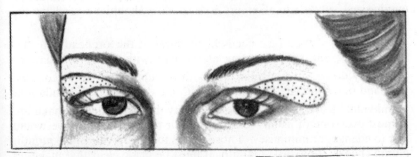

For an oriental look, draw the line slightly extended at the outer corners, giving an almond shaped effect.

To bring out pale, sunken eyes, use a light shade of foundation over the sunken area. Very light shades of colour should be used close to the lashes. Eye liner and mascara should be used on the upper lashes only.

For eyes that are too big a very fine line can be drawn along the upper lid. This sounds easy, but it is not. The line must be so fine that even

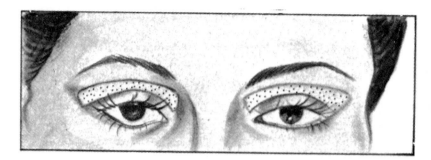

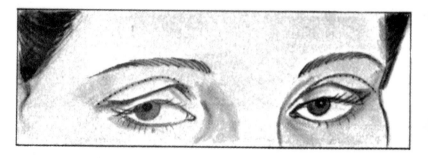

with a hand mirror, nowhere on the skin should the actual line be visible.

In order to achieve this effect, a fine eye liner brush should be used over the upper lid, at the point where the eye lashes meet the skin (the actual line is more on the hairline than on the skin). Large eyes are normally considered signs of beauty in India, and their effect should be emphasized subtly for glamour. Eye shadow should be used on the upper lid only.

A diamond shaped face needs highlighting at the forehead with the lighter tone, and slight shading at the chin with darker foundation.

To play down a rectangular face both the upper and lower corners, jaws and outer forehead are shaded with the darker toned foundation.

Individual features can also be helped by the art of illusion make up. Almost everyone of us has some feature or the other, which we would like to change, or minimise—a nose that is too big, a very small mouth, plump cheeks; a big broad mouth. It must be made clear that make-up does not change the face physically. It merely gives the impression of having done so.

With a little bit of knowledge and knowhow, you can look like what you would like to look like, without any problem.

For a short, wide nose, foundation that is two shades darker than the skin tone should be applied at the sides of the nose from the eyebrows to the nostrils. If this is not possible, use a foundation a couple of shades

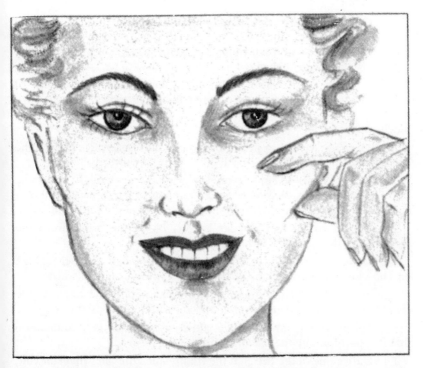

lighter than your skin tone. Streak down the centre of your nose, from the bridge to the tip. Be careful to apply under the tip also.

In order to make a long thin nose look broader, use a foundation—one or two shades darker than the skin tone, under the tip of the nose. A pug nose can be made to look softer by using foundation one shade darker down the top of the nose and on the edge of the nostrils at the lower end. Be careful that there is no line of demarcation between the lighter and darker shades, otherwise the illusion is lost.

If your nose is very large, you can make it look less conspicuous, by using powder, a couple of shades darker than that, on the rest of the face.

A dark shade of powder is useful for reducing puffiness under the eyes. On the other hand, if there are dark circles and dark rings, lighter coloured foundation and powder effectively conceal the haggard look.

Very round eyes can be elongated by drawing a faint line from the outer edge of the eye and fading it away gently so that there is no perceptible ending.

Eyebrows are very important in the art of illusion make up. You are to make sure that they are well groomed. They form an exotic frame for the eyes and must be kept in perfect balance with the shape of the face.

If the facial cut is round, it would be a good idea to have a sharp arch.

On a heart shaped face, the brows should be plucked and made a little thinner and longer. In order to balance a square jawed face, the eyebrows should be a bit heavier—beginning slightly outward from the outer corner of eye pencil.

Rouge is one of the most useful and effective agents in the art of illusion make-up. If used brightly, with knowledge and care, it can work miracles. If misused, it can spell disaster. A great writer once said: "Too much rouge is a sign of despair"

To make a square face appear more round, place the rouge high on the cheekbones and blend it smoothly and softly downwards.

To disguise a double chin, apply the rouge very sparingly under the chin line to make a soft shadow, and so minimise the fullness. Another method would be to cover the under chin with a darker foundation.

To make a round face appear longer, blend the rouge from the cheekbones downwards, fading gently outwards.

For a long face, rouge should be kept to the top half of the face, high on the cheek bones and blended softly upwards and outwards.

The oval face needs no disguises and tricks. Apply the rouge to the cheekbones and blend it upwards and outwards towards the temples.

Besides providing an attractive glow, rouge can join foundation shading to remould the facial outline.

These are some of the tricks of the trade—pick the ones that suit you, highlight your good features and disguise your weaker ones.

Brown is beautiful

THE best make-up for brown skins would be colours from pale beige to rich brown, since dark skins need shades to complement their skin tones, whether it veers more towards deep brown or pale ivory.

Choose a liquid foundation which matches the skin colouring. A dark skin seems to show or give the impression of oiliness because of the way light reflects on the skin. To reduce this unwanted sheen, a good water-based foundation is essential. If this is not available in the right shade, choose a shade slightly darker, but never lighter than your own skin tone.

Dark skins show up layers of make-up more than fair skins, so a sheer foundation is best. If the exact shade you would like is not available, choose a shade closest to the skin colour of your neck and add a little distilled water to make it more translucent.

Dark circles around the eyes can also be played down by using a foundation—one shade lighter than the one you use for the face. Pay special attention to the blending, so that there is no line of demarcation between the two shades used.

Brown mascara looks beautiful on brown skins, but very few people realise this. Outlining the mascara should be a fine black line. A black eye pencil rimming the eyes can give a stunning impression.

Soft eye shadow in brown giving the winged doe-eyed look would be excellent. This should blend into the upper brow bone, from a soft brown to a soft brick brown. The blending must be perfect. Soft brown eye shadow used on the lower lashes would complete the entire effect.

Many girls concentrate on the upper lid and tend to overlook the lower completely. Kajal helps to accentuate the Eastern look and dramatises the eye make-up because of its jet black shade. In order to achieve a longer lasting eye make-up effect, a brown-skinned girl should first use a cream or liquid eye-shadow and then intensify it by adding soft powder shadow to match.

A dark lipstick on very dark skins can look overdone and overpowering. A less glossy mattecolour, very near your own natural lip tone, gives a gentler look. For the day, a translucent lip gloss is best and for the evening, a deep maroon would look beautiful. Any colour in pink or coffee caramel should be avoided by dark skins.

Where lips have pigmented into a dark brown, a cactus cleanser, followed by an almond lanolin cream, used for a period of six to eight months would have a gentle lightening effect.

It is also important to use a foundation under the lipstick. Very often people with dark skins have blackish lips, because the colour of the lips, in contact with the ultra-violet rays of the sun, causes photosensitisation, ultimately blackening them. A lip gloss over the lipstick would help to highlight the intensity of colour.

I feel that on brown skins, intense, bright, hot shades of blush on gives a vibrant look. If a brown girl has a dry skin, a gleamer should be used at night and the colour should be more red than pink. For the day, a soft tawny rose would look best.

If her skin is oily, she should use unfrosted natural—coloured blush on for the day and reddish shade for the night. All shades of peach should be avoided. Brown blush-ons or gleamers should be used only for reshaping the face, or to create an illusion.

The sheerest, finest texture is best for dark skins. Apply the powder with a soft brush or fresh cotton wool. It is important to buff off excess powder from the face to avoid patchiness or a clogged look. Choose a colour that matches closely the colour of your neck. A translucent, colourless powder plays up the natural colour of the skin.

Although every skin needs general cleansing and protection, dark skins need a greater amount of moisture. Surface drying is more obvious on dark skins because the cells that are ready to flake show up more. For this reason a dark skin must be heavily moisturised to protect against natural elements that draw out moisture.

Oiliness in certain areas has to be kept under control with a combination skin treatment. I have often been asked whether a dark skin needs protection from the sun.

A dark skin can be exposed to the sun for greater periods than a fair skin, without tanning or burning. It is very rare for very dark skins to sunburn. Melanin, the deep brown to dark pigment which is responsible for the colour of the skin, screens out most of the sun's burning rays.

The degree of natural protection is proportionate to the amount of melanin present and the evenness of its distribution. The more the melanin, the darker the skin tone and less apt to burns. It is interesting to note that very dark skins show signs of ageing slower than fair skins.

However, dark women have to guard against the tendency towards scarring or discolouration of their skins, as these would be more apparent with their colouring.

Another problem is that dark skins appear to heal at an accelerated rate, and this action can produce an excess of scar tissue known as keloids. Although keloids can be treated, they may not be removed completely once they have formed. It is important to cleanse the skin daily without too much rubbing.

Blemishes need treatment immediately, and one should.be careful with acne preparations as discolouration with dark skins shows up in cosmetic surgery. Dermabrasion, or chemical peel is a risk because there is the possibility of pigment change and of the formation of keloids.

As already mentioned, the most essential thing for dark skins is moisture. This can be obtained either from the atmosphere or from good moisturising creams. It is moisture which helps the skin to look smooth and healthy.

If the skin is dry, it needs a moisturising cream, or lotion, to replenish natural moisture loss. If there are areas which are somewhat oilier, the skin would still need moisturising in whatever form that suits your skin ype. A dark, dry skin would require proper cleansing at night with a moisture-based skin food.

Before bedtime, the skin must be thoroughly cleansed of all cream, with moist cotton wool. Dry cotton wool absorbs moisture from the skin, dehydrating it further. The neck and arms can be left with cream all night, but the face and the region around the eyes should be cleansed of all cream before going to sleep.

HEALTH AND FITNESS

Balance your Diet with Natural Foods

ACCORDING to Dr Roger Williams, the renowned bio-chemist "Faulty cellular nutrition of one type or another may be a basic cause of most of the non-infective diseases."

In other words, he stresses the fact that our tissue cells should receive all the elements that are needed to resist diseases and thus ensure a healthy body. The daily diet is, therefore, extremely important, as we can supply our bodies with the essential food elements that are vital to good health.

This, in turn, will reflect not only in terms of combating disease, but also in terms of better performance and an attractive appearance. Good health, in fact, reflects best on our external selves. . . . on the skin, the hair and figure.

Diet and nutrition experts are in agreement that only a balanced diet can supply the body with adequate amounts of the essential food elements. They also emphasize the fact that a variety of natural foods can give the diet the best 'balance' that is required. This is because natural foods are the best sources of food elements.

When we talk of natural foods, what exactly do we mean? We mean foods that have a high nutritional value, without being too high in calories, or cooked in a way that destroys the nutritional content and upsets the balance of the digestive system.

Foods that are raw and fresh, foods that are simply cooked and those that are neither refined nor processed, would fall in the category of natural foods. Through such foods the body is able to get enough nutrition without any detrimental effects on health.

Foods that are refined or processed, cooked in too much oil, fat and spices can be very filling, as they have high calories, but hardly have any nutritional value. Many natural food elements are removed through processing, refining and cooking. These play havoc not only with health, but also with the beauty of the skin and hair, not to mention the figure.

The key to good nutrition is a balanced diet—one that supplies the body with the essential elements in the right proportion. The diet should, therefore, consist of a variety of foods that provide proteins, carbohydrates, fats, vitamins and minerals.

Proteins are essential as they help to build and repair the body. They can be obtained from lean meats, liver, egg and fish. Meats that contain excessive amounts of animal fats should be decreased.

Proteins are also available in lentils, peas, beans, nuts and whole grains. Milk and milk products provide us with proteins as well as minerals, carbohydrates and fats.

The way these foods are consumed is of great importance. For instance, cottage cheese (paneer) and yoghurt are ideal ways of taking foods that are beneficial to health, in terms of good nutrition, yet without excess fats or sugar.

In choosing cereals, opt for those that are whole grain products, so that the essential food elements are present. These also provide maximum dietary fibre that is essential for the body's efficient elimination of wastes. Refined grains do not contain the necessary 'bulk' nor the essential elements in adequate quantities. White bread and polished rice are refined cereals, which should be substituted by whole wheat and other whole grain products.

Canned, processed and bottled foods should be avoided in favour of fresh fruits and vegetables, so that the body receives the valuable vitamins. The more we take our foods raw, the more 'alive' the vitamins remain. Vitamins are so sensitive that many of them are destroyed through cooking.

Fruits and vegetables also supply enough natural sugar and carbohydrates for the body's requirements, apart from vitamins, minerals and enzymes. Citrus fruits, tomatoes, cabbage, melons, sprouted grains, seeds and beans are rich natural sources of Vitamin C that the body needs daily.

Vitamin C is not only destroyed by heat, but is not stored by the body. It is needed to keep the tissues strong and healthy and to build up resistance against disease.

Green, yellow and leafy vegetables are good sources of Vitamins A,B, and E. These should be either eaten raw or cooked simply—steamed, baked or poached, using very little water.

It is important to remember that vitamins are necessary for the absorption and utilization of many minerals. Thus a variety of natural foods can help to correct deficiency diseases like anaemia.

A bowl of fresh salad consisting of raw carrots, cucumber, tomatoes, radish, cabbage, lettuce etc. should form a part of the daily diet. Mix sprouted grains with this and use lemon juice for natural flavouring and taste.

Fresh fruits are so versatile—they can form ideal appetisers, between meal snacks and substitutes for rich desserts. Fresh fruit juices should be taken instead of bottled or canned drinks, which are high on sugar and low in nutritional value. Besides, these also contain chemical essences, preservatives and synthetic colours.

Snack foods, like biscuits and cakes add only empty calories, while fresh fruits for rich desserts can help to start a new eating pattern that is bound to pay high dividends in terms of better health.

Right eating, therefore, is absolutely indispensable and right foods are those on which the body can attain maximum health. If we want to look and feel our best, we have to take the trouble to find out about ou; body and its needs so that we can supply it with the right nourishment.

Concentration on heavy, over-cooked foods does not give the body a chance, either to be healthy, or to look its best. If people keep off sweets, ice cream, chocolates and soft drinks, there will be fewer skin and weight problems. On the other hand, making sure that you and your family are being brought up on a variety of fresh, natural foods is the basis of good health.

Vitamins may come to us in pill and capsule form, but the true value of an orange or a carrot, in terms of nutrition and good health, has not yet been duplicated even by the most advanced laboratory.

The Advantages of Raw Foods

WE usually associate the term 'good health' with freedom from disease. Yet, a person who does not show the symptoms of any disease may not be truly healthy. Inspite of the sophisticated developments in medicine and medical techniques, the incidence of disease has been increasing. Today's killer diseases are mainly degenerative—cancer, heart and circulatory ailments, respiratory disorders, diabetes, etc. Even mental depression and disorders are on the increase. The cause lies mainly in our lifestyle—our sedentary occupations, overeating, little or no exercise, exposure to pollution and chemicals. After a lifetime of damage to our bodies, we can hardly expect medicine to reverse the degeneration.

The answer lies in taking a step towards 'positive health'—a term that I would like to use for a condition when the body has high vitality and greater resistance to disease, so that the degenerative processes are kept at bay, preserving the body's youth and vitality for a longer time.

For this, we need to look at a few nutritional facts. Research has indicated that when nutrition improves, so does health. The quality of food that we eat is most important. We may be eating a 'balanced diet', but the balance may be between highly processed and over-cooked foods, both of which lead to the destruction of many food elements.

The more we go towards fibre and fresh raw foods, the closer we come to positive health in terms of nutritional quality. Raw foods from plants contain many active substances that have been seen to play a disease- prevention role. They also strengthen the immuno system of our bodies. Foods like fresh raw fruits and vegetables, fruit juice, grains, sprouts, honey, yoghurt, etc., contain properties that can even reverse bodily degeneration.

Research in raw food has included the treatment of people already suffering from degenerative diseases, who were kept on raw food diets. The results were encouraging enough for scientists to conclude that health improves when the quantity of raw foods in the diet is increased. The advantages are many.

— The vitamins present in raw fruits, vegetables, sprouts are preserved in their original biochemic forms. Cooking destroys or damages the vulnerable vitamins. Moreover, vitamins do not function in isolation. They need each other. While scientists have isolated a number of vitamins, many more exist. Raw foods contain these. Thus, they ensure the intake of all necessary vitamins and other elements.

— Raw foods are the sources of valuable minerals, some of which are available only in raw foods.

— Heat destroys enzymes. Some raw foods like cabbage, turnip, sprouts, etc., have been seen to encourage the formation of enzymes in the body, protecting the liver.

— Intake of fibre found in unprocessed foods leads to more roughage and bulk, improving the process of elimination of wastes. They also have more nutritional value.

— The intake of raw foods cleanses the body of toxic wastes and restores the acid/alkaline balance of the blood. Cooked food increases the level of sodium, while raw foods help to maintain the sodium/potassium balance.

— — Bioflavinoids, or pigments that occur in raw plant foods are known to prevent diseases, including those caused by bacteria, fungi and viruses. They are easily destroyed by cooking.

— The trace elements are also found in raw plant foods. They are needed by the body for biochemical reactions.

Together with wholesome cooked foods, your diet should include a variety of raw foods. Gradually increase the quantity of raw foods. Fresh fruit and vegetable juices should be taken. They not only contain valuable vitamins, minerals, enzymes and trace elements, but aid the removal of toxic residues from the body. The raw foods you should take are fresh fruits and vegetables, sprouted grains, nuts, herbs, peas. Include yoghurt. Take fresh green salads. Cabbage, cucumber, lettuce, tomatoes, fresh peas make good salads, with some sprouted grains. Garnish with herbs, lemon juice, and vinegar. Slices of fruit added to the salad make it more appetizing. With a little experiment, you can discover your favourite tastes and flavours.

Nature intended us to have positive health. That is why she has provided us with such a vast variety of foods with high nutritional value.

How to Stay Slim

ONCE the desired weight is reached, keep an eye on your weight always. It is much easier to get rid of the odd pound than to have to lose it all over again.

Slimming is worth the effort. You feel healthier, increase your chances of longevity and also look and feel attractive.

Organise your day and keep yourself busy so that you don't lounge about the house constantly fixing yourself snacks. It is an excellent idea to either:

a) Fast completely one day in a week.

b) Fix one day in the week when you will only take liquids.

c) Fix one day in the week when you will take only fruits and raw vegetables, or for that matter anything in natural form.

d) Miss one major meal. Select whichever method you find most suitable. Office goers can have a glass of juice or a sandwich rather than a regular lunch.

e) Once a week have just one boiled meal of chicken, mutton or eggs. The idea behind this diet is that when no fat is eaten, body fat is churned to convert the protein into blood. Hence, the more protein you eat, the slimmer you get.

It is true that water drunk during the day helps in fasting. A heavy intake of water during the course of the day helps to freshen the stomach and kidneys. Constant care must be taken during slimming to avoid constipation. About the best would be to have spinach mixed with a bowl of yoghurt.

In addition to dieting, regular amount of exercise is essential to keep the body muscles from getting flabby.

A low calorie intake reduces weight but does not lower measurements. What actually tightens muscles is proper exercise. Otherwise you would have a soft, flabby, unproportionate body. If you have grown out of your measurements, rather than ordering a new wardrobe, make a desperate effort to go back to your initial size. The moment you have a whole new wardrobe made to fit your new measurements, the desire to go back to where you were, automatically decreases.

It is a good idea to have regular weekly facials especially during the time you are slimming. If you have joined a beauty clinic, consult the beauty therapist. When the body loses weight it shrinks just as a balloon does. It is essential that the skin should not lose its natural muscle tension. It is a bad idea to nibble during the day. It is necessary to fix hours for meals and the proper time for resting the stomach. Like every other part of the body the stomach too needs a break.

It is a good idea to start lunch or dinner with a bowl of salad. This will cut down the desire to overeat.

Diet And Exercise

THE word diet has almost become synonymous with losing weight. Strictly, it should imply what one should eat to keep the body in perfect form and fitness, but most of us immediately associate the word with eating programmes that are designed to shed weight.

This is because excess body weight is probably the most common problem today. People are involved all the time in all kinds of methods and gimmicks to lose it, which are either not very successful, or quite dangerous to health.

Crash diets or diets that are restricted to one category of foods are bound to have detrimental effects by creating deficiencies of one or more of the essential food elements.

There may be some initial weight loss, but one is, very soon, back to where one began, because these 'diets' differ from the usual eating pattern. It becomes quite difficult to wage this battle for long between oneself and one's habits. One ends up losing both heart and health.

Eating is really so much a matter of habit. We continue eating the foods we have been brought up on.

The cause for excess weight is as common as the problem itself taking in more calories than the body burns up in daily activities. In other words, if you have been eating more than what you need, you are bound to be overweight, unless you suffer from a glandular or other diseases.

Excluding these instances, most cases of overweight are caused by over-eating. Those who have been through everything—from calorie counting to starvation—may have realised that the only diet plan that works is one that is based on good sense.

If the daily consumption of food is a balanced one, you will be taking in the right number of calories. It is not only possible to lose weight, but to keep it to the desired level by eating a balanced diet. This can only be done by bringing about a gradual change in eating habits.

While habits really persist, crash diets and other gimmicks never do. Skipping meals never works. If you go without breakfast and end up with a huge dinner, you are approaching the problem in a manner that is eventually self-defeating.

Eating is dictated by hunger and appetite. Hunger is a basic urge that fulfils a physical need, while appetite can make you eat even when you are not hungry. Appetite is stimulated by the smell and sight of food, and not by the physical need. There are also many compulsive eaters who feel the urge to eat when they are emotionally tense or upset, or even bored. They take to overeating as a means of compensating for their frustrations.

So you may first have to analyse your own behaviour and habit patterns to try and understand why you eat even when your urge is not being dictated purely by hunger. Sooner or later, you may find that it is actually much easier to satisfy the hunger than the appetite. Once you can identify your weaknesses, it becomes easier to control them.

Bringing about a change in eating habits is easier said than done. A radical change can never be achieved overnight. The change must be gradual and to do this you will have to take a look at what you eat. See the eating patterns you follow and learn a few facts about food. You may find that a gradual cutting down on quantities may solve your particular problem. Or you may try eating the same things cooked in a different way. For instance, changing from your usual fried egg to a soft boiled one, cooked in the shell, will decrease your calorie intake. Reduce your normal two spoons of sugar in your coffee to one. Perhaps, with time you may even be able to coax yourself into giving up the coffee habit and keep to fresh fruit juices and buttermilk. Think what you will be losing in terms of weight and gaining in terms of good health.

Allowing these little changes to creep in will help you to gradually break your food habits.

Have fresh fruits instead of exotic puddings for dessert. Include a bowl of raw salad with your meals, consisting of fresh vegetables and fruits, leaving out rich dressings. Lemon juice, spicy tomato juice (fresh) and vinegar make delicious dressings. Leave out the gravy. Avoid deep fried foods. Have them boiled, baked, or roasted and remove all traces of visible fat before eating. Yoghurt, clear soups, fresh fruit juices and fruit 'chaat' can all be wonderful low-calorie fillers.

Fruits and vegetables contain enough natural sugar to give your body what it needs. These gradual changes will, over a period of time, produce weight loss without causing deficiencies of any of the valuable food elements and nutrients... and your new eating habits will help you to maintain your new weight.

You will also have to pay attention to your basic meals. You must make sure that what you eat provides your body with adequate amounts of the essential nutrients. This calls for a little calorie consciousness. There are vegetables that contain very few calories, but are full of vitamins and minerals. Some of them can be eaten raw, while others can be simply prepared without rich gravies. You can eat plenty of these—like cabbage, cucumber, lettuces, sprouted grains, capsicum, radish, spinach, string beans, turnip.

There are other vegetables, from which you should have one daily helping, choosing from tomatoes, carrots, pumpkin, peas, leeks, squash, beet.

Among the other foods, you have to ensure adequate protein intake by eating lean meats, chicken, fish, egg, with lentils, milk and milk products.

Meat has a high-calorie count, but you can remove visible fat and avoid rich gravies. Among cereals, you can have a lightly buttered toast

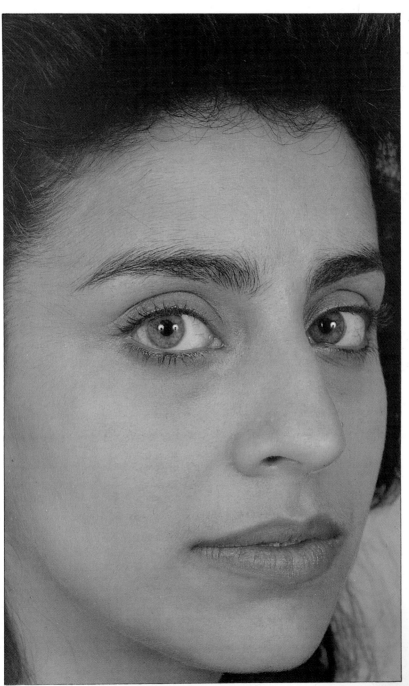

WITHOUT MAKEUP

EYE MAKE UP

Apply eye shadow
Outlining with eye liner
Apply Mascara
A made up eye

MAKE UP FOR THE LIPS

Outlining with a lip pencil

Filling in lipstick

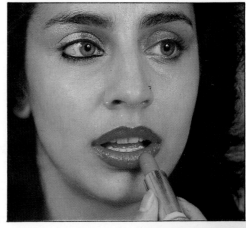

Finally the lip gloss

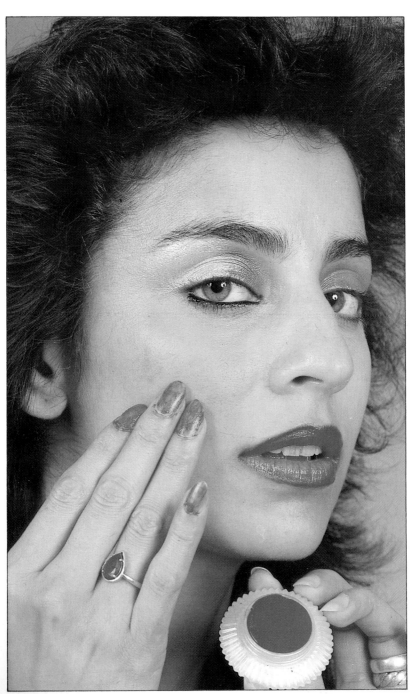

ROUGE BLUSH ON APPLICATION

at breakfast, 2 small chappaties or a cupful of cooked rice at meals. Whole grain products have fewer calories but higher nutritional value.

Fruits for desserts will gradually remove the need for sweet dishes, which only provide excess sugar and starch. Fruits like pears, oranges, grapefruit, watermelon, papayas and grapes contain enough natural sugar and plenty of vitamins and minerals.

The real challenge is maintaining the weight loss. Eating, reducing and staying slim should be a pleasant affair and not purely a tug of war between you and your will power. Hunger is a physical need that must be satisfied. Denying it means actually going against your body. Healthy eating is basically a matter of learning how to answer this need in an ideal way. It calls for an intelligent selection of foods and preparations that satisfy both hunger and the palate. At the same time, it should help to maintain both form and fitness.

A very important point to remember is to take your doctor s advice before going on any kind of reduction plan, to ensure that you will be getting all the essential nutrients.

A few basic facts, a little effort and a sensible calorie budget will give you many more years of the youth and beauty that comes from sheer good health.

It is important to note that most reducing plans call for the intake of 1,000-1,200 calories a day for women, and about 1,600 for men. The calorie intake required, however, differs with each individual, and his or her occupation and style of life. For instance, a career woman would require more calories than a housewife. Similarly, a man with a sedentary occupation, say an office worker, would require a smaller calorie quota than a manual labourer or a sportsman.

The popular belief that any "fattening" food eaten is immediately converted into fat has no scientific base. The cause of obesity need not be the fat intake alone. In the case of an extremely active person, little fat will be deposited. However, a lady of leisure, gorging herself on cakes and cookies, will have fatty layers deposited all over her body.

It is a good idea to look scientifically at the facts of gaining and losing weight. The food you take into your body each day is like fuel and your body uses as much as it needs for the days activities. The surplus is stored. Keep in mind the fact that the human body is very thrifty. No food that enters the body is ever wasted. The digestive system processes every particle, the liver converts it and the body stores it away as fat.

The body has three levels of storage. A certain amount it keeps in circulation as glucose—blood sugar—for immediate use. The next level of storage is in the form of body starch-glycogen. The third, long term fuel storage form is fat. This is nature's most compact form of stored energy.

It may be worthwhile to note that it is not always fatty intake that is converted into spare tyres. Any food, even protein, taken in excess of body needs eventually ends up as stored energy, in the form of fat. These are simple facts which have been scientifically proven.

Women have a tendency to retain fluid in their body tissues, and this adds both weight and inches. These are the first to disappear when you begin your reducing plan. That is why the results of a short fad diet are gratifying. But the moment the programme ends and you resume old eating habits, the fluid again seeps into the tissues, and you are back where you started.

In most of the quick reducing plans, you do not make even a dent in the amount of body fat. All you do is lose water. If you drink two glasses of water and stand on the weighing machine, you will find that you have gained a pound!

An increase in weight can be due to a variety of reasons, and it is best to consult your physician for advice. The numerous causes may include childlessness, frustration and unhappiness, alcohol, menopause, glandular imbalance of the thyroid, amongst others.

It can even be traced to the time the children became self-sufficient, or to when the family acquired a second car! At this stage, new goals and new interests are needed. Psychiatric advice and care can be of great value in such instances.

Fasting For Health

MANY of our religious rituals are based on scientific principles of good health, although most of them have become so steeped in superstitious beliefs that the original ideas on which they were founded have become lost and forgotten.

Fasting is one of the common practices. It originated as a means of restoring, rejuvenating and preserving good health. In ancient India, regular fasting was followed by enlightened sages as a method of internal purification, based on the idea that when one fasts, the body processes are allowed to rest. Specific principles were laid down to make the method really scientific. The sages, with their own powers of vitality and higher consciousness, knew that it was not just fasting, but a method of controlled fasting that must be followed. The purpose that they intended to achieve could be termed as autolysis.

Autolysis is a natural process of self-cleansing or self purification. The principle itself was borrowed from nature, which goes through a process of self-cleansing by a systematic removal of impurities.

Our bodies become laden with accumulated toxic wastes and must be cleansed internally, or washed thoroughly, in order to carry out their normal functions. Regular controlled fasting, by drinking raw juices of fruits and vegetables, was advocated, to cleanse or wash the body of accumulated toxic wastes and debris.

This helps to strengthen and refresh the processes of the body, not only by cleansing the system, but also by providing the much needed rest to internal organs, leading to better health and performance.

Autolysis is said to benefit the body in several ways, the main advantage being that it brings about overall good health.

The blood stream carries nutrients and oxygen to all parts of the body. The purity of the blood is very essential for good health and vitality. However, very often the blood stream contains impurities which may be harmful to the body and even the brain.

It was believed that a clean flow of oxygen and nutrients could be promoted by cleansing the blood stream through regular juice fasting. It would not only benefit the body, but improve the thought processes as well. Thus the vitality of both the body and the mind are promoted.

The endocrine glands, which regulate the flow of hormones are also cleansed through autolysis and perform their function by promoting the flow of hormones. This helps the body to be renewed. Washing away accumulation of wastes improves the functioning of the nerves, soothing them and bringing about a sense of relaxation and mental well being. At the same time, the senses are rejuvenated and sensory organs improve their functions.

The accumulation of wastes can actually cause a feeling of fatigue and listlessness. Once the wastes are removed, muscles are relaxed and free, allowing the body to eliminate waste and toxins. Autolysis promotes the functions of the skin, especially in elimination.

This itself cleanses the skin and allows pores to breathe, freely, bringing about a radiant glow. Thus it can be seen that the body as a whole benefits through self-cleansing.

In order to follow the method of autolysis, or juice fasting, a few points must be borne in mind.

First, you must consult your physician to ensure that the body is free of any specific disease, or disorder that requires treatment. This is particularly important.

Secondly, autolysis is not being advocated as a method of weight reduction. It is based on some specific principles, which should be adhered to. For instance, it advocates drinking of raw juices of fruits and vegetables. This would naturally eliminate tea, coffee, canned juices or aerated drinks. Tea and coffee contain acid and would actually detract from achieving the objective. It is not just a question of taking in fluids, but drinking juices of fresh fruits and vegetables.

Vegetables and fruits contain valuable vitamins, minerals, amino acids, enzymes and other elements that actually aid the process of elimination of toxic matter from the system. Taking these in the form of juices also helps the digestive system to get a rest from the daily task of digesting solid food.

The extracts of fruits and vegetables may be suitably diluted with water. There are enough to choose, oranges, apples, pineapples, melons, carrots, tomato, etc. Lemon juice can also be had, or added to vegetable juices as a flavouring.

The raw juice fast is advocated one day per week. There is another aspect which should be kept in mind. This is the question of what constitutes the diet during the rest of the week. If your diet during the week consists of rich carbohydrates, fried foods, heavy desserts, you will actually be loading your system with toxins and defeating the purpose. Autolysis can hardly work the expected wonders. It may be all right to cheat once in a while and give in to temptation, but as a rule, you should see that you take in enough natural foods daily, as well as follow a few basic principles of healthy living, like regular exercise and adequate sleep. Autolysis certainly helps, but you should give the system a chance.

The ancient system of juice fasting and self-cleansing is being followed in several modern health centres in the West, which are based on natural healing principles. It is part of a programme to restore health and vitality to the entire system.

The programme also includes simple exercises and steam baths that are actually geared to aid the process of elimination of wastes.

Controlled juice fasting is followed one day in the week. Such natural healing centres devote themselves to healing the whole person, rather than a specific complaint, by promoting better physical and mental health. Many people join these supervised programmes from time to time to restore and rejuvenate themselves. Autolysis helps to create a feeling of mental well-being and youth, by promoting good health. This itself is a great advantage in the stress-laden world of today.

Get into Shape

THE only way to achieve and maintain a good figure is to exercise regularly.

Most of us have at least one area that poses a problem. Although it is possible to lose weight through regular exercise, it is the firmness and tone of the muscles that gives the figure good proportions.

Weight has a tendency to accumulate in certain areas of the body and the best way to get rid of those bulges is to concentrate on exercising that particular area.

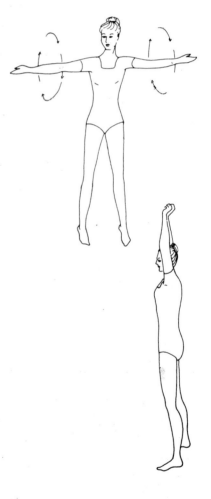

There are different exercises for different areas... for trimming the waist, tightening the stomach muscles, slimming legs, thighs or hips.

Your exercise routine should begin with general limbering up and then proceed to the trouble spots. Exercise your figure into shape.

Arms: The upper arms tend to get flabby and acquire unsightly bulges. The following exercises will help:

1. Stand with the feet slightly apart. Stretch your arms out to the sides, with palms facing upwards. Rotate the arms in small circles, clock-wise and then anti-clockwise. Repeat this twenty times each.

2. Stand with the feet slightly apart in a doorway. Clench the fists and, raising your arms overhead, touch the door frame. With the palms facing upwards take a deep breath and press against the frame as hard as you can.

Abdomen: This is one of the most common problem areas.

1. Lie on the floor on your back, with feet together and arms at the sides. Lift the legs a little above the ground and hold to count ten. Repeat. Gradually the count can be increased as one gets used to the exercise. Do this five times to start with, then increase gradually.

2. Keep lying on your back. Bend knees and keep feet flat on the floor. Raise the body to a half sitting position with arms stretched out before you. Consciously pull in the stomach muscles. Lower the body and repeat.

This exercise should be done very slowly. Start by doing it five times, increasing gradually to ten times.

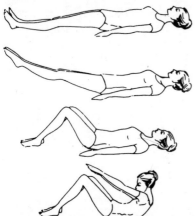

Hips: 1. Lie on your back. Roll hip to the right side. Try to touch the floor on the right side with your left foot. Do the same on the left side, touching the floor on the left side with the right foot. As you roll from one hip to the other, the hips should get the brunt of the movement.

2. Lie on your back with arms stretched out to the sides. Bend knees and bring them towards the chest. Roll your hips to the right so that the right knee tries to touch the foot. Back to position and repeat on the left side. Return to position and repeat five to seven times on each side.

Rear: This is another common problem spot.

1. Lie on your stomach. Rest your chin on your hands. Lift up one leg at a time, without raising the hips off the floor. The leg should be held straight. Repeat this five times with each leg.

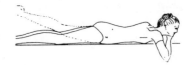

Thighs: 1. Lie on your right side, leaning on your elbow. Place the left hand on the floor, palm downwards, in front of your chest. Lift your left leg about 8 inches off the floor and hold it. Supporting yourself on the hips, elbow and hands, raise your right leg to try and touch the left foot, return both legs one by one to the floor. Repeat this seven to eight times and then turn on your left side and repeat.

2. Lie on your back with legs stretched out. Supporting yourself on your elbows, lift the

back up from the floor. With toes pointed, bring the left knee towards the chest while the right leg is stretched out on the floor. Straighten the left leg and lift it up towards your head as far as it can go. Bend knees again and repeat five times. Do the same with the left leg.

Waistline: These are excellent for making the waist trim, supple and flexible.

1. Sit on the floor with legs spread slightly wide. Raise arms up and keeping them straight, bend from the waist first towards the right, then towards the front, to the left and back again to position. Repeat this five times, starting with the right side and then five times starting with the left.

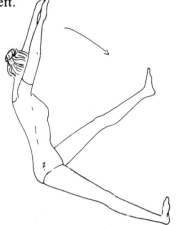

2. Stand with feet slightly apart. Bend from the waist to the right. As you bend, the right arm should relax by your side, while the left arm is resting on your head. Bend as far to the right as you can. Repeat this to the left in the same way, reversing the arm position. Do this five times each side.

Bustline: The breasts themselves contain no muscles. They are supported by the pectoral muscles. These are to be exercised.

1. Join the palms together at waist level, with the elbows out. Press the palms together for a count of ten. Now bring palms

up at bust level and repeat. Relax and repeat.

2. Lie on the floor, with arms extended upwards. While keeping them straight, cross them in a scissor movement till you feel the pull of the muscles.

3. **Stand with feet slightly apart.** Stretch arms out to the sides and rotate them, making wide circles, first clockwise and then anticlockwise. While doing this exercise, shoulders should move too.

Before you begin any exercise schedule, remember to consult your doctor.

Yoga

YOGA is an ancient Indian discipline that deals with the entire well-being of man. It is the traditional path to physical, mental, moral and spiritual good health. It has gained relevance today, as a means of attaining a well-balanced personality, which can cope with the stress-laden lives we lead.

The word 'Yoga' actually means union. Here, it signifies the union of body and mind. The discipline has often been misunderstood to be purely mystic, involving bodily contortions. In actual fact, it has a scientific basis and consists of well-defined exercises, which have precise results.

It was Patanjali who first described the 'Eight Limbs' of Yoga, around 200 B.C., which led to the understanding and realisation of the Self. These are:

Yama: moral commandments

Niyama: discipline

Pranayama: control of breathing

Pratyahara: freedom of the mind from the senses

Dharana: concentratiqn

Dhyana: meditation

Samadhi: state of super consciousness

Thus, the mind is free from the senses, the emotions and passions are controlled and the body is kept strong and healthy. The ultimate is to reach a level of consciousness of the inner self through concentration and meditation.

Among the many Yogic paths, it is Hatha Yoga that is popularly practised. It deals with physical exercises, entailing the assumption of postures, or 'asanas', as they are called. Pranayama, or control of breath, is combined with these. The 'asanas' involve static positions, when a particular pose is held for a prescribed duration of time. During this time, the mind is disciplined, as it concentrates on parts of the body. At the same time, the body, including the nerves and muscles, are exercised. Thus, the mind is used to discipline the body, benefiting both.

The exercises take the body through:

— standing poses, to improve suppleness and posture. Between other standing poses, the basic standing pose, or 'Tadasana' is repeated;
— various sitting postures, which exercise all parts of the body and improve bodily functions, as well as physical strength and fitness. These include 'Sarvangasana', or shoulder stand, and 'Halasana', or plough posture;
— ending with 'Shavasana', or corpse pose, which aids recuperation. It calms the mind and brings about complete relaxation. At the end there is a feeling of physical and mental exhilaration.

There are numerous benefits to be gained from Yoga. To name some:

— Improves suppleness and grace
— Improves posture
— Tones and relaxes muscles
— Improves circulation and hence oxygenation
— Keeps the spine flexible
— Alleviates physical aches, like back ache
— Helps to cure insomnia and mental depression
— Aids digestion and relieves constipation
— Soothes the nerves
— Induces relaxation of body and mind
— Releases mental tensions
— Relieves fatigue and allows recuperation of energy.

Yogic exercises can easily be included in any exercise programme, but they should be learnt under supervision and guidance, because it is necessary to master the technique before regular practice is begun. The body should not be subjected to any strain. Remember to consult your physician before taking it up. Yoga is a convenient form of exercising too. It does not require any gadgets or equipment. The 'asanas' can be performed in less space. They should be practised in a well-ventilated room, wearing loose clothing to allow stretching. The feet should be bare.

Meditation

HAPPINESS has almost become synonymous with material success, so much so, that a considerable amount of physical and mental energy is directed at achieving it. This is just as much a phenomenon of modern day living as the degenerative diseases, which have been accepted as ailments of the times. Somewhere along the line, we have become so involved in the effort to achieve our goals, that we have forgotten that the mind and body were not made to cope with such stress and strain. At the same time, we seem to have realised that happiness is not material fulfilment, but complete freedom from the desire to achieve it. It is only when the mind is free from the craving for material and personal welfare, that the mind can be at peace. This realisation brings us face to face with another kind of pursuit—the search for harmony—for, it is the discrepency between our desires and their fulfilment that throws us out of harmony with the environment and gives rise to feelings of discontent, frustration, fear and anxiety—what is now known as 'stress'. The outcome of this has been an arousal of interest in the philosophy of meditation, which has its roots in ancient India. Meditation is said to be the route to a mind that is free of all fears, possessing an inner strength and gradually leading to a harmonius existence.

The mind has various facets. One of these is a higher mind, or a spiritual mind, which has the capacity of both thought and action. What we do not know is how to use this mind to improve ourselves and our lives. This is like having a confirmed belief in the existence of a supreme power and yet, not knowing fully what it is, or how to bring it into our daily experience and thus enrich our lives. The higher mind is asleep within us and meditation helps to awaken the sleeping mind and bring it into a state of consciousness. Let us call the mind 'consciousness' and say that the purpose of meditation is to awaken a sleeping consciousness.

The philosophy of meditation is based on the belief that the answer to the search for harmony lies, not in the environment, but within the 'self' and that one gains a deeper knowledge of the environment through the search for the 'self'. It is a kind of 'insight'—looking within to gain a clearer view of the self. This can be done by first separating oneself from the environment, resulting in a clearer view of it. This helps to reveal our fears, anxieties, priorities, goals, in relation to the self, helping us to look at them in the true perspective.

The first step towards meditation is concentration, or contemplation. This helps the mind to develop a state of receptivity. It can be said to be a simpler form of meditation. One can sit in a natural, relaxed position, close the eyes and concentrate on something. For instance, one can recall past events in their order of occurrence. This is like picturing them with the mind's eye. The philosophy of Yoga advocates the 'Lotus' position, which allows a relaxed position, when the mind and body are relaxed, but alert.

An easier way to discipline the mind and help concentration is to focus it on an aspect of the natural world. For instance, one can think of a beautiful spot, with green fields, trees swaying in a mild breeze, a gently flowing stream and so on. This gives the mind a larger sphere to concentrate on, within which it can move from aspect to aspect, but is confined within the boundaries of this imagined picture. Or, one can concentrate on the Sun, which is the most essential part of life. Think about a particular time of day—the rising Sun, perhaps. The mind can actually picture it—the warmth, the light, the golden glory, our need of it, the Sun as the giver of life. This way, we allow related thoughts to flow through, gradually finding that this contemplation has actually helped the mind to relax and brought it into a state of receptivity. Concentration, therefore, disciplines the mind, and allows it to rid itself of trivial thoughts and teaches it to dwell on important ones. Just this discipline can increase our efficiency in our daily work.

It is true that when one first starts to practise concentration, the mind begins to wander within a minute or two. One can either bring the mind gently back to the subject of concentration, or stop it for the time being and begin it again at some other time of day. Gradually, the mind gets trained to concentrate for longer periods. All this while one has been making the effort to concentrate. When this effort finally ceases, the mind can concentrate *effortlessly*. It is then that the mind becomes a void, allowing the higher mind to enter, flowing freely.

Let us go back to the scene that we had pictured with the mind's eye. The scene was quite panoramic. Gradually, as one practises day by day, the boundaries should close in—that is, one should gradually eliminate details and come closer and closer to a central point. Thus, the scene gets smaller and less panoramic and the mind is gradually disciplined to concentrate within a smaller sphere, leading to a specific point—like the blazing Sun, or the snowy peak of a mountain.

Apart from being the route to meditation, concentration has other benefits. It helps the mind to free itself from distractions, improves the memory, decreases tensions and, most important of all, leads to self-knowledge. The Hindu philosophy of meditation involves using the art of concentration to attain a state of consciousness called 'samadhi', where the void is created, allowing the higher mind to enter. Spiritual thoughts flow through into expression. This is a state of super consciousness. This kind of meditation is learnt under the guidance of a 'guru', or teacher.

The spiritual, or higher consciousness has no limits, making the mind aware of things that are beyond our knowledge. It imparts an inner wisdom that is not related to any acquired beliefs or ideas. These periods of meditation, or introspection, prepare the mind to receive spiritual thoughts. It is an experience that is not related to the environment at all. It takes place within the 'self'. It illuminates the self and helps us to know the inner self, thus revealing our hidden fears. Only when this revelation takes place can we know how to discard our hidden fears. This experience is said to be highly stimulating, leading us to greater harmony with our environment, to a state of complete harmony.

The Hindu philosophy advocates the use of sound to facilitate concentration and meditation—with the use of the word 'Om', which is repeated over and over again, in a low voice and a rhythmic manner.

Learning to practise concentration with impatience will only lead to failure. It requires great perseverance. There may be no immediate results. On the other hand, it is possible that changes are experienced quite early. One should not be discouraged, because the relaxation of even a few minutes by concentration brings a sense of peace. Start by concentrating for two or three minutes at a time, two or three times in the day. Gradually, increase the time. Soon you will find that you do not have to make the effort to increase it. The mind gets gradually disciplined to concentrate for longer and longer periods, when it is able to keep out all external distractions and influences. You should be sensitive enough to recognise the change it can bring—till a time when one discovers that it has helped to change one's entire life, making it much richer and certainly more meaningful. It can be an experience of 'fulfilment', which no material achievement can ever bring.

Correct Breathing...
Nature's
Key to Good Health

THE ancient Yogis of India had advocated principles of good health that are being recommended and followed today. Correct breathing and its benefits is one of them, which was recognized long ago as being a method of cleansing and purification of the entire system. Many yogis seem to exude a vitality even during their old age, mainly due to the fitness of their bodies and a healthy mental outlook. While, on the other hand, there are younger people, confined to desk jobs, leading sedentary lives, who are overcome by feelings of fatigue and exhaustion. They are prone to many nagging physical complaints and fall prey to diseases caused by their living habits. Perhaps, we are more in need of adopting these principles of good health than those ancient yogis were!

It has been acknowledged that proper breathing and breathing exercises are of great overall benefit to health, as it affords a means of cleansing the body of accumulated wastes and toxins. In fact, the daily practice of correct breathing is reputedly able to conquer problems like insomnia, loss of appetite, poor circulation and generally lead to better health and better performance.

Oxygen, after all, is 'life' to all the cells of the body. When we breathe in, oxygen passes into the blood stream and when we exhale, the lungs give out carbon dioxide that the blood is carrying... and this 'washes' the body internally. If this process is carried out in the proper way, the internal washing is bound to be more efficient. The yogis lay emphasis on the fact that oxygen is the best blood purifier and the most effective means of cleansing the circulatory system. They stressed that through this kind of internal cleansing, the respiratory system is strengthened, the digestive system improved and consequently, the body is invigorated and acquires a vitality.

The Yoga practice of 'pranayama' is probably one of the best exercises of correct breathing. Devoting a few minutes each day affords a means of natural cleansing of the system. Exercises based on 'pranayama' are being followed at health centres in many parts of the world. They are as follows:

1. Close one nostril with the fingers. Then breathe in through the other nostril. The air should be inhaled in short sniffs. Then close the second nostril and breathe out. Breathe in again through the other nostril. Alternate it up to ten times. This exercise not only purifies the blood stream, but also cleanses the entire filtering process. Complaints such as sinusitis are said to be alleviated too.

2. Sit on a chair that supports the back comfortably. Allow your chest and abdomen to relax completely. Pull in the abdomen with a sharp movement and breathe out through the nose and mouth. Then allow the abdomen to relax while you breathe in. This may require a little practice. It should be a continuous process for 3 to 4 minutes.

3. Whenever you can, while walking or standing, exhale air in short breaths through the mouth, with the lips pursed.....as one does while whistling. Then inhale by taking in short sniffs of air through the nose.

One of the main benefits of physical activities like jogging, or skipping, is that it allows the body to inhale as much oxygen as possible—provided the air is free of pollution—a phenomenon that the ancient yogis did not encounter! It is essential to bear in mind the correct methods of breathing during such activities. The air should be inhaled deeply through the mouth and nose. Very often, some exercises cause a tendency to hold the breath. This should not be done, unless the exercise specifically requires it. When you hold your breath, pressure builds up inside the chest and can interfere with the return of blood to the heart.

Many people suffering from chronic fatigue, or common ailments, have reported the beneficial results of performing a few breathing exercises early in the morning, in the open air. These can be done in front of an open window:

Stand with your hands on the lower ribs and breathe in deeply through the nose, very slowly. When you have taken in as much air as you can, breathe out through the mouth, exhaling all the air.

Those who have included breathing exercises in their daily lives have not only experienced renewed physical vigour, but also relief from mental stress and tensions. In fact, it has improved their thinking capacities and enabled them to deal with their work more efficiently. This is probably due to the fact that the brain cells are most sensitive to the shortage of oxygen. Many physicians believe that fatigue and exhaustion are mentally, not physically, induced problems. When mental stress is relieved, the feeling of fatigue will be absent.

Yogic breathing exercises, practised daily, are also reputed to rejuvenate the mind through the fresh flow of oxygen into the blood stream. Based on these simple principles of correct breathing, many exercises have been devised to cure respiratory disorders, like bronchitis and asthma. Various health clinics have included these exercises in their programmes, with diet, rest and relaxation, thus providing an answer to many modern-day problems.

Ancient India was replete with many secrets of good health that were practised at a time when modern day drugs were nonexistent. Today, medical advancement has provided a great deal of knowledge, which helps us to acknowledge the benefits of these ancient principles. Internal cleansing of the body is even more important than external cleanliness—and correct breathing is a key to a body and mind that are sparked with vitality.

Re-Posture Yourself

OUR bodies were made for movement—yet, everything we do seems to be geared to keep us out of it! The result is that we not only develop health problems, but present an appearance that is far from flattering. Beauty is a total effect. It includes not only the way you look, but the way you move, walk, sit and stand. This is where a good posture counts. Graceful, elegant movements, sitting and standing postures, poise and selfconfidence are all important aspects that go to make up the total 'you'. You should take a candid look at your reflection in the mirror and see how others view you. Do you slouch? Do your shoulders sag? Does your body need reposturing? It is possible to learn how to move, sit and stand correctly and bring your body to its natural alignment and keep it supple and straight.

The first thing is to be more aware of yourself—the way you breathe, the way you hold yourself, whether relaxed, or tense. Many of us keep our muscles habitually tensed and thus stifle breathing. Some of us may have straightened the posture to the point of arching backwards, while others may be slouching forwards, with curved spines. Ideally, an imaginary line, going straight down your side from the top of your head, should bisect your ear, shoulder, hip joint, knee and ankle. The way to go about it is to 'free' yourself from a bad posture habit and clear the body of habitual tensions. Some experts feel that the posture of the body is related to mental attitudes and reflects our "psychological history," our sensitivities, bad memories, or wounds. They feel that this can block the flow and spontaneity of our movements.

A good posture depends on the right use of the abdominal muscles. When we stand, the weight should be evenly distributed on both feet. The body should be held straight, without being stiff and rigid. Hold the abdomen in, with the shoulders down and slightly back. Practise a standing posture before the mirror by standing correctly for a few minutes daily. The spine should be upright in a natural way, without tension. The same goes for the sitting posture. When you walk, the basic standing posture should be adopted, but the weight should be forward on the front foot. The arms should swing slightly and the toes should point directly forward.

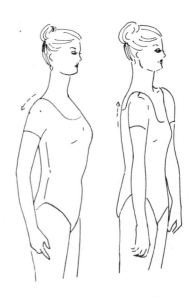

Some exercises have been developed to improve the posture. While exercising, there is no need to hurry through the movements. The pace should be slow and the breathing should be deep and rhythmic. Try to make the abdominal muscles work. When you lift your leg, lift from the abdomen and when you turn your body, turn from the waist, so that the abdominal muscles are used.

The body, like every object, has a centre of gravity, with the body weight evenly distributed around it. The more even this distribution is, the less strain on the muscles. The posture that allows perfect balance is one where the spine curves naturally—slightly forward in the neck region, backward at the upper back and slightly forward in the lower back. This is supported by the pelvis, which curves backward. If you consciously try to adopt this balance and then practise it, the posture will improve. There will be less strain on the spine and the body will be able to carry its weight better. If this basic posture is adopted and all movements, like walking, lead from it, the body will have better alignment. Those who wear high heels for long periods, tend to bend slightly forward, with the lower back curving backward. This puts a great deal of strain on the spine and muscles. They should practise the standing posture and then walk holding the same posture, allowing the arms to swing in a natural, gentle manner. Practise this with the feet bare.

Your work may entail sitting for long periods of time. You will find that you habitually bend forward, and keep the head down. This puts a strain on the neck and upper back. Consciously, try to keep the back upright, holding the head up. If you must bend forward, do so from the hips. Daily stretching exercises are very useful for people with sedentary jobs.

An exercise programme that helps the posture can be adopted after consulting your physician.

1. Begin with this exercise, as it helps relaxation. Kneel down, stretch the arms forward, keeping them flat, palm downward on the floor. The fingers should be spread. Drop your head down between your arms and keep it relaxed. Using the abdominal muscles, arch the back and pull forward, again using only abdominal muscles. The head should still be dropped forward. Drop down again slowly. This should be done in one smooth movement.

2. Lie on your back with the legs bent at the knees. Lift legs slowly, knees still bent, holding them at an angle to the body. The lower back should not be raised at all. Come back to position.

3. Still lying on the back, stretch one leg out, the other bent at the knee. Raise the stretched leg up, using abdominal muscles. Swing the leg over your head as far as possible. Lower slowly and repeat with the other leg.

4. Sit up. Stretch your arms forwards holding a magazine. Roll slowly down backward only up to the tail bone and go back to position. Down again, up to the waist and back to position. Finally, go down to the shoulders and

come back to position. Keep your eyes in front of the magazine right through. If you find it difficult at first, bend your knees slightly.

5. Take a short rod and sit with the legs far apart. Keep the feet flexed. Hold the rod over the head, then slowly bring one end of the rod down across in front of you. Put it up again and then bring down the other end. Elbows and waist should be straight and all movements should be by the abdominal muscles.

Mystery of Sleep

SLEEP is a complicated process that is even now not fully understood.

Does a human body actually need sleep? Frankly, there is no scientific data to prove that it is necessary. Although many gadgets have been discovered to electronically monitor the brain, the actual need for sleep has not yet been proved.

New York psychiatrist, Dr. Weinberg who is an expert on sleep, says: "We still do not know when sleep occurs in the brain. No sleep centre has yet been uncovered. The body does not rest, but you can rest without sleeping."

What we do know, however, is that some people toss and turn, with tired bodies, but their minds alert, hearing the clock ticking away the hours tell them that they need sleep. On the other hand, there are those who fall asleep very easily.

Sleep occurs in three distinct phases. The pre-dormitum stage, sleep proper and the post-dormitum stage.

During the first stage, our bodily processes begin to slow down and breathing becomes more shallow. The muscles relax. The temperature and blood pressure fall slightly and, although we are by no means fast asleep, we are certainly not wide awake.

Suddenly, quite unconsciously, we cross the border line into sleep proper. For those who suffer from insomnia, the pre-dormitum stage lasts several hours.

Dreaming is as natural a process as sleep is. But is it necessary to dream? Medical opinion is unanimous on the point that dreaming is necessary. Dr. Weinberg says that "dream activity is essential to mental health".

Although the exact function of dreaming has not yet been specified, there is scientific data to prove that dreaming provides a safety valve to anger, anxiety, fear and other emotions. It also helps to sort out emotional problems.

One fascinating theory is that dreaming helps the mind to sort out thoughts and impressions collected over the day and reorganise itself for the next day, retaining whatever information it regards necessary. Dreaming, it is believed, helps in the perfect balance of the central nervous system.

Since it has been found that there are rapid eye movements during the process of dreaming, dream sleep is known as REM sleep. It may appear lighter than dreamless sleep; it is actually deeper and more refreshing.

As a rule, most people normally forget their dreams unless they are awakened during, or immediately after the REM sleep.

It is fascinating to note that all human beings live according to a specially designed natural body rhythm. It is a sleep dream cycle in which 90 to 120 minutes of sleep alternates with 5 to 10 minutes of dream period.

In the event of the mind suddenly wandering off or falling into a happy reverie, there is no cause for alarm. It is most natural. In fact, even day dreaming is not just a phrase, or a style of speech, but a fact supported by scientific data.

Interfering with sleep, as long as it is not too often, has been proved to be harmless. If dreams are prevented, one can have 15 to 30 dreams together, known as the rebound phenomenon.

Barbiturates and alcohol prevent the natural dream sleep cycle and are potential dangers, in the long run. The suppressed dreams increase slow wave (dreamless) sleep, at the cost of REM sleep, which is vital to mental health.

The more the body cycle is disturbed by tranquilisers, the harder it is to regain the normal process. In fact, chronic insomnia is often the result of long usage of drugs and sedatives, which were initially prescribed to help sleep.

Deep sleep is not really necessary for the body to feel refreshed. A normally healthy body puts in about 15 to 20 movements every night. Movement of the body is only normal during sleep. It helps exercise the muscles and ease blood circulation.

In every human being there is a 'sleep point'. It is up to every person to discover this sleep point. If yours is 11.30 p.m. and the late show film ends at 12.30, that means you have missed the 'moment' and you will have trouble falling asleep, even if you are feeling tired.

You may often notice that you are feeling too exhausted to even sleep. Sometimes exhaustion acts adversely. Instead of dropping off to sleep immediately, the mind gets overactive, while the body is drained of physical energy.

There are some points to remember regarding sleep:

1. Your sleep attitude is more important than anything else, including artificial measures.

2. The best method of taking care of your sleep is to use the hypnosis therapy.

3. Insomnia is actually worsened by the anxiety about not getting enough sleep, night after night. Try to relax, without thinking of when sleep will overtake you.

4. Try not to make bedtime a time for recalling all the ills of the day and the tasks to be faced tomorrow.

5. Try reading a book—it may help to steer your thoughts into one channel.

All About Stress

STRESS is not a new word. It is just that it has assumed newer and greater dimensions in the context of the modern day world. When people talk about the 'stresses of life' and the 'rat race', they are referring to the increased economic pressures, job anxieties, marital problems, which have all assumed greater proportions in today's world.

The competitiveness in life has increased so much recently, that even children are pushed too hard and too fast to cope with the pressures of studies and examinations. As for adults, they live in a state of non-stop hurry. The strain of all this rush and frustration is the root cause of many nervous and psychosomatic illnesses.

A baby when hungry is in a state of stress and so is a schoolboy faced with a difficult question paper. A businessman caught in a traffic jam, or an older person concerned about his health, may both be under stress, though the stress will be of varying degrees of intensity and significance. The period between the onset of the condition when the body is alerted to the change or threat in the environment, up to the time when the threat is removed, is known as the state of stress. It is the price we have to pay for having a highly responsive nervous system and for living in a challenging world.

The age-group with the greatest risk from stress is the 35–50 bracket, when the flexibility of youth begins to wane and yet when career and financial challenges are at the maximum.

As age advances, a person becomes less capable of dealing with stress, but fortunately, there is a counter-balancing force. Ambitions and responsibilities are less and so are demands and challenges.

On the other hand, even young children are faced with stress, when they are set goals by their ambitious parents and chronic stress of this kind can lead to severe problems during adolescence.

Stress can be physical and psychological and it is those with a psychological bias that are not so easily dealt with. Short term psychological stress can be dealt with by 'thinking over the problem' or discussing it, but when there are continuing marital, economic or occupational problems, stress is not easily removed and affects the sufferers' mood, personality and even health.

Short term stresses have few symptoms—ranging from a quickened pulse to 'butterflies in the stomach', which have no far-reaching consequences.

Long term stresses have dire effects in a number of ways and produce more enduring symptoms-like sleeplessness, inability to concentrate, unsociability, irritability, high blood pressure, ulcers, heart trouble. These symptoms are the physical manifestations of mental up-heavals. In fact stress, as the cause of increase in heart attack, becomes a matter of much concern.

When a person is chronically frustrated in his attempts to find a solution to his problems, the period of stress lasts for a long time and a number of long term changes occur in the body and its organs. This includes an increase in the level of cholesterol or fatty acids in the blood, which can lead to sudden death.

Cholesterol is a life-giving substance which is pumped into the blood at a high level by the adrenal glands. When there is psychological stress, a high cholesterol level is maintained, especially when there is no physical exercise to reduce the level.

Consequently, the fatty acids are deposited on the walls of the arteries, leading to high blood pressure. An individual under constant stress is, therefore, slowly impairing blood circulation in the body and when there is a major or sudden emergency, the arteries deprive the heart of blood resulting in a coronary attack, which can be fatal.

It is generally felt that women are less prone to stress than men. The reason for this may be because of biological and social differences, which push men and women into different life style.

Men are cast in the role of the breadwinners and their goals are very different from their female counterparts. For the women, the goals involve bearing and rearing children. As long as both are able to meet their goals, they are free from stress.

However, psychologists feel that there is greater stress among women because of their emancipation, leading to the situation where their roles are not very clearly defined.

Very often she faces a conflict between her natural responsibility of child rearing and her state of emancipation, where she is assuming more responsibility outside the home. Stress complaints associated with menopause are also common among women.

Almost all of us, at some stage have felt inadequately equipped to deal with the stresses and strains of life. If you have this 'I can't cope' feeling, it is not a sign of weakness at all. It simply means that you, together with millions of other people, are finding it difficult to adapt yourself to the strains and stresses of modern life.

Though it is not possible to remove the strain or stress, it is certainly possible to see the causes more clearly and to learn how best to cope with them. Emotional outbursts and loss of temper actually lessen pressure, but this is hardly the ideal way of dealing with the problem. It needs only one member of the family to be tense and before long others are affected in the same way.

If we are to be happy and healthy, we have to defeat stress and it can be done—the answer is relaxation. It means learning the scientific way of relaxing so that every organ, every cell is given the opportunity of being re-charged with strength and vitality.

Yoga is an excellent way of relieving strain and the first step in Yoga is learning to breathe better. Breathing exercises are very helpful. Practise breathing-in slowly and steadily through the nose. Let the ribs expand naturally and effortlessly. Hold the breath as long as it is comfortable and then breathe out through the mouth. Do this regularly.

Walking is also very good exercise. Good sleep is not, however, the answer to stress. In fact, ten minutes of complete relaxation while you are awake, is worth a whole night's sleep. The complete mental and physical stillness of waking relaxation is a very effective 'rest-cure'.

The ideal times for relaxation are the first thing in the morning, the last thing at night and at midday (to give yourself a break). Never allow less than five minutes for effectiveness.

Start your day with a good all over stretch as soon as you awake. Even yawning is good exercise! An important part of learning to relax is in practising it with enjoyment, concentration and faith.

To set about trying to learn to relax with impatience or scepticism, or to practise it as a duty, is asking for failure. This is where the mental discipline comes in. Stress is like any other emotion—the more you know about it, the more you can control it.

What Women Must Know

DURING the different stages of a woman's life, the breasts undergo many changes.

Puberty brings on the first sign of approaching womanhood when breast growth begins. Later, during the months of pregnancy many more changes occur, bringing with it the fulfilment of motherhood, in which the breasts play a significant part.

As the years pass, they begin to manifest the fact that the ageing process has begun, by losing their firmness and resilience.

Apart from learning what kind of care you can give them to keep them beautiful, it is also necessary to have a knowledge of the conditions they may be prone to in terms of problems and diseases.

Everyone of us must know how to recognise a few danger signals and abnormalities, so that we may get help in good time.

Indeed, cancer of the breast is the most frequent malignancy that occurs in women. A little awareness goes a long way in terms of protection, while early diagnosis of breast cancer can even save your life.

The breasts consist mainly of glandular and fatty tissues. The amount of fatty tissue varies from woman to woman and determines the size of the breasts.

The mammary glands consist of lobules that enlarge to hold milk during lactation. The breasts begin to enlarge during puberty, increasing in size during pregnancy and lactation and decreasing in old age.

The breasts also contain a large number of lymphatic vessels which pass to the lymph node in the armpit.

Every woman should examine her breasts every month. Any skin changes should also be noted, with changes in their shape and size. A lump or a cyst may just be a benign tumour, but it should be reported to the doctor immediately. There are many kinds of benign tumours of the breasts, but this is for your physician to decide.

Examine yourself every month just after the menstrual period. The best way to do this is by palpation of the breasts, with the flat of the hands, keeping the finger-tips together. Examine the upper part, the central and the lower parts, as well as the armpits.

Visual examination in front of a mirror helps to observe changes in size or outline, as well as any changes on the skin surface.

Some of the signs that may be danger signals, are certainly worth knowing. These are puckering of the skin, any discharge from the nipples, lumps, cysts or swellings, changes in the shape or size.

If there is pain that is not the normal pain that occurs before menstruation, it should be reported to the doctor. Regular self-examination of the breasts also helps one to become familiar with one's own normal size, shape and consistency, so that changes, if and when they occur, are more easily noticed.

Annual routine medical check-ups should also be undertaken. This is of particular importance after the age of thirty. The chances of malignancy increase with age and are more likely during middle age.

Self-examination and detection is one of the most effective ways by which possible malignant conditions are diagnosed and treated. Early detection has a very high cure rate—about eighty per cent.

If malignancy spreads to the lymph nodes, cure becomes more difficult. That is why it is important for women to be aware of these simple ways by which they can protect themselves.

The best way to examine yourself is to lie flat on a firm bed and then palpate the breasts with the flat of the palms. Changes in size and outline can be detected by observing the breasts in the mirror.

First with your arms at the sides and then with the arms held up over the head. While doing this, see if there are any changes in size, outline or skin surface.

The breasts have also been one of the most important criteria for judging the beauty of the female body. A loss in firmness or resilience causing the breasts to droop, therefore, becomes a matter of great concern to women.

The breasts themselves contain no muscles. The bustline may, however, be protected, or lifted, by exercising the chest and shoulder muscles.

During pregnancy, the breasts increase in size. This may also happen if there is weight gain. The skin stretches and the breast tissue lose their resilience.

The increased weight during lactation causes the breasts to sag, unless proper precautions are taken, by way of exercise, proper support and massage. Exercise is indeed an effective way of keeping the breasts from drooping and improving the bustline.

Beautiful Mother-To-Be

IT is a wonderful moment in the life of a woman when she discovers that she is going to be a mother. Mingled with the feelings of excitement and anticipation, are twinges of doubt that the coming of the baby will mean a complete change in her appearance and way of life.

But, if you are a normal healthy woman, there is no reason why a natural event like having a baby should cause any apprehension or upset you in any way. It is true that the body goes through many glandular and hormonal changes which do affect the skin, hair, weight and figure. It is also true that knowing how to cope with these changes will help you, not only to enjoy your pregnancy, but to look and feel your best. Looking beautiful makes you feel beautiful, and feeling beautiful makes you look a little more beautiful!

Actually, pregnancy can do wonderful things to most women. Changes in the hormone producing glands can benefit the skin, making the complexion clear and fresh, adding a glow to it. There is also the tendency to become more relaxed and tranquil.

Changes in the skin do not take place very early in pregnancy, but as time passes, women with dry skins may find their skins getting drier. Since dry skins are prone to wrinkles, it is necessary to take daily care by having a programme of cleansing, toning and nourishing.

This can be done by using creams which not only moisturise the skin, but also cleanse and nourish it. The use of a pre-bath gel will help to keep the skin soft and protect it from the dehydrating effect of soap and water.

Another fairly common problem is chloasma, or the 'pregnancy mask' as it is called. Chloasma is a pigmentation of the skin, which may disappear at the end of pregnancy, but very often the condition may persist, extending from spots and patches to a dark mask. If this happens, it is necessary to consult a beauty therapist. The sun's rays aggravate the pigmentation of the skin—it is, therefore, imperative to use a protective sun-screen cream before going out in the Sun.

The formation of stretch marks on the abdomen and the breasts is a routine occurrence during pregnancy. As the name suggests, it is caused by the over stretching of the skin, when rapid weight gain is followed by weight loss in pregnancy. The genetic factor is also important—some women develop stretch marks more easily than others, under similar conditions.

Care should be taken in early pregnancy by gently massaging the skin with a pre-bath gel to make the marks less apparent. It will also keep the skin soft and moisturised. The skin on the abdomen can get very dry during pregnancy, causing itching, while scratching the area will make the marks more defined. The application of the cream should continue after the confinement, so that stretch marks that have formed can lighten considerably, even if they do not disappear completely.

If you have a greasy skin, you may find that spots and blemishes have cleared during this time. However, sometimes women complain of an increase in the oiliness of the skin. For excessive oiliness, very thorough and regular cleansing is the first way to keep the skin free of blackheads.

Pay attention to your diet by eliminating fried foods, chocolates and cola drinks, by reducing carbohydrates and sugar and including fresh fruits and vegetables. If there is an increase in pimples and acne, consult a therapist for cleansing, toning, removal of blackheads, medication and remedies for closing the pores and reducing the oiliness of the skin.

Unless you wish to shout from the rooftops about it, you can actually keep your pregnancy a secret till the fifth month. Obviously, as time passes, you will lose your slim figure, but make sure it is temporary. Weight gain during pregnancy starts around the third month due to an increase in the size of various organs, like the uterus and the breasts. The total weight gain differs from woman to woman, but should not be more than about 10–12 kgs.

The first thing to do is to see that you are eating the foods which are part of a well-balanced diet. The 'eating for two' concept is outdated. What is important is that you get adequate nourishment in the form of vitamins, proteins and minerals for your own and your baby's well being. Your doctor will prescribe vitamins, calcium and iron supplements to check deficiencies and the baby will help himself according to his requirements.

Too many of us have a diet rich in carbohydrates, without realising that a balanced diet is very important. You should have proteins, fresh fruits and vegetables, moderate amounts of carbohydrates, fats and adequate fluids. Very rich foods should be avoided during pregnancy, as many women are prone to digestive disorders during this time.

Exercise is another way to check excessive weight gain. Women, who are not used to physical exercise should not exercise at this time. Needless to say, exercises which results in exhaustion and fatigue should not be undertaken. If you are not excessively overweight and lead a life of normal activity, it is not really necessary for you to exercise. In fact, it is just as important to have adequate rest. Walking is probably the best exercise, not only does it benefit the figure and general health, but maintains muscle tone and keeps them in good condition.

Changes in the breast also take place during this period. There is an increase in both the size and weight of the breasts. The breasts do not contain any muscular tissue, so it is necessary to give them adequate support to prevent sagging. Once they sag, it is difficult, in fact impossible, to restore them to their former shape.

Many women hesitate to breast feed their babies, thinking that it will cause sagging, but breast feeding itself does not cause sagging—it is neglect and improper treatment that does. A supporting brassiers is very important during pregnancy and lactation, to give support to the breasts and to the shoulder muscles which support the breasts. The support should be from above and below. Change the bra size as the breasts enlarge. It is more important to invest in good brassiers than in clothes during pregnancy.

This brings us to the question of your wardrobe. Good grooming is just as important when you are pregnant, especially to keep your confidence and morale high. Maternity smocks are very useful for lounging around in the house, visiting friends informally and shopping. When you want to look more elegant, wear colours and materials that are more flattering. Your intention is not to conceal your pregnancy, but to make it the most memorable time of your life. Dark colours in prints and plain materials are more flattering. Low narrow necklines or V-necks will help to detract from the bulk.

Another problem which can become cause of great concern is hair loss, especially after childbirth. The activity of the hormone producing glands can add an extra gloss and sheen to the hair, but this is temporary. About six weeks after the delivery, hair can begin to look lifeless and dull. Post-natal hair loss is almost routine and is due to iron and vitamin deficiencies and hormonal imbalances.

When a woman is pregnant, the baby draws upon her reserves, causing deficiencies. A diet with adequate supplies of iron, iodine and Vitamin B will help cases of falling hair. Iodine improves the circulation of blood to the scalp, helping to accelerate the growth and replacement of hair. Your doctor can also prescribe Vitamin A to help the texture of the hair.

Apart from daily care, your hair may also need a tonic treatment to regain its health. However, most women need never worry about going bald—their hormones take care of that. But, as all of us know, well-groomed shiny hair is an essential part of looking beautiful.

Many women get complacent and tend to let themselves go during pregnancy, thinking they will catch up with beauty afterwards. The coming of the baby will mean a real change in your daily schedule— your day will revolve around the baby's schedule, leaving you with less time to spend on yourself. Now is the time to start your beauty routine, paying special attention to personal cleanliness and hygiene.

And remember, that not only now, but right through your life, a little effort and daily care helps to prevent most beauty problems. In fact today's beauty message is prevention, not cure.

So, carry on with your normal activities, keeping to a balanced diet, adequate sleep, fresh air, exercise—all of which contribute towards a healthy, youthful and more beautiful you.

AEROBICS

UNLIKE machine that wears out with use, the human body thrives on physical activity and movement. In fact, without constant activity, the body deteriorates, both in efficiency and appearance. The benefits of regular vigorous exercising has evoked a great deal of interest in recent times, with increasing evidence that a high level of physical fitness allows the body and the mind to function at their peaks, bringing about a sense of general well being and a positive feeling about life and living. It was during this increasing awareness of the benefits of dynamic physical fitness, that Dr. Kenneth Cooper's new concept of exercises created a great impact. To him goes the credit for the term 'aerobics'.....a name which caught public attention and, probably, started the jogging boom!

Aerobic exercises are so called because they require a steady flow of oxygen and are based on increasing the demand for oxygen. Dr. Cooper, himself, defines them as "a variety of exercises that stimulate heart and lung activity for a time period sufficiently long to produce beneficial changes in the body". When the demand for oxygen increases, the consumption of oxygen also increases. The efficiency of the heart and lung improves and thus the body's ability to utilize oxygen is increased. Not only is blood delivered more efficiently and rapidly to all parts of the body, but the blood is 'purified', being more oxygenated. The enthusiastic response that this new concept received was because it was "the first scientific attempt to validate and quantify the effect of exercise", as claimed by Dr. Cooper. The medical world is also looking at aerobics with much interest, as it is found to play a preventive role in heart disease. With the strengthening of the circulatory system, the heart is able to pump more blood with less effort and thus becomes more resilient. In other words, the circulatory system becomes used to performing under stress conditions and can, therefore, cope better at times of emotional or physical stress.

Aerobic exercises involve the following:
1. Breathing in large amounts of air, or oxygen.
2. The body uses more oxygen at a faster rate.
3. Increasing the maximum amount of oxygen that the body can process at a time.
4. Using large muscle groups of the body in a rhythmic and sustained manner, over a period of time.
5. Exercising vigorously for at least 20 to 30 minutes.

While performing the rhythmic and vigorous exercises, the pulse rate and breathing become more rapid. Measuring the pulse rate helps to determine if the exercise routine is suited to the individual level of fitness. It also helps in establishing a 'pulse rate goal'. The Stanford University Heart Disease Prevention Programme has suggested the following pulse rate goals:

Age 20-29: 138–142 beats per minute
Age 30-39: 130–134 beats per minute
Age 40-49: 122–126 beats per minute
Age 50-59: 113–117 beats per minute
Age 60-69: 105–109 beats per minute

The pulse rate goal is bound to vary, as the maximum individual heart rate declines with age.

The increase in pulse rate and breathing during exercises gradually lead to the strengthening of the respiratory and circulatory systems. The changes that are induced in the organ systems are called the training effect. This training effect can, therefore, be achieved by exercising at least 3 to 4 times a week for 20 to 30 minutes at a time. Aerobic exercises have been developed so as to suit all age groups, since they are 'age adjusted'. Followed properly, according to the rules, aerobics can be the channel to dynamic fitness.

Apart from improving the efficiency of the respiratory system and the heart, aerobics have several other advantages:

— The general circulation and muscle tone improves. So does the function of the body's cells, as more blood and oxygen is carried to the tissues;

— Increases vitality and prolongs the youthfulness of the body. Lack of exercise hastens the ageing process;

— Increases energy and stamina;

— Causes loss of body fat. Physical activity for longer periods helps to burn stored fat and this improves the appearance;

— Improves bodily functions;

— Improves sleep and helps to cut down on tea, coffee, drugs, alcohol and cigarettes;

— Relieves mental stress;

— Increases the flexibility of the body;

— Improves general appearance and look by improving the figure and the skin.

Walking, jogging, running, cycling, skipping, rowing, swimming are all aerobic exercises. So are many kinds of sports, like tennis. These activities involve the use of large groups of muscles in a rhythmic and steady manner, during which a demand for more oxygen is created and breathing becomes rapid. Of these, swimming is most ideal, as it involves the use of more groups of muscles and also stretches them. However, not all have access to a swimming pool. Any of the other activities can be taken up.

The routine of aerobic exercise should follow a warming-up session, since the body should not be put through a sudden bout of strenuous activity. The body should be warmed up so that there is no strain on muscles and joints. Five minutes of stretching exercises, or calisthenics, help to increase the suppleness of the joints and muscles. Toe touching exercises, sit ups, push ups, side bends, are exercises that can be done before aerobics. Similarly, there should be a period of cooling down after aerobics, so that the body is made ready for rest. The body has to be brought down to normal after heightened activity. This can be a five-minute period of walking or slow jogging, so that the body is gradually brought to rest. Only after the body has cooled down and perspiration stopped, should one take a shower.

Aerobic exercises can be performed at any time of the day, except immediately after a meal. There should be an interval of two hours after the meal. It is better to exercise at the same time every day, as this helps to establish a habit pattern and maintain regularity. Regularity is one of the most important factors. In fact, irregular exercising is worse than not exercising at all. A few other points must be borne in mind before adopting aerobics:

— Some age restrictions must be observed by those who have not been exercising regularly;

— It is essential to have a medical check-up and obtain your doctor's approval before adopting an exercise programme;

— The effort that is put in should be gradually increased, so that excessive strain and fatigue are avoided. Start slowly at first, and gradually increase the effort in order to accommodate the programme that helps to reach a higher level of physical fitness.

Most important of all is to develop a positive attitude about physical fitness. Once the body gets used to the movement and activity, exercising can become a pleasure, rather than a boring routine. Those who have achieved dynamic fitness have experienced a sense of total well being and vitality that makes one happy just to be alive.

Cosmetic Care for Men

SHACREAM
SHABASE

TILL very recently beauty treatments were considered a woman's prerogative. A beauty salon was entirely the woman's domain. Things have changed. The way women have entered nearly every professional sphere that was dominated by men, beauty care is no longer purely a feminine pastime. The mushrooming of men's salons is evidenced enough. Today's man is fully aware of the importance of his external appearance and is convinced that it does not begin and end with the clothes he wears. He is slowly, but surely, shedding the idea that beauty treatments detract from masculinity. He knows that in this competitive world, a youthful appearance is certainly a plus point. He is keen to delay the signs of ageing, and why not? This trend of thought has led to the development of various cosmetic aids for men.

A man's skin is just as vulnerable as that of a woman. Exposure to the sun, to central heating, air-conditioning, pollution, all influence his skin and cause it to become dry and irritated. If the skin is not protected and the dryness persists, the signs of ageing occur prematurely. Therefore, like women, men should be aware of their individual characteristics and adopt daily care routine that are suited to them.

Men are ardent followers of the soap and water ritual. Most soaps can be harsh on the skin, due to the detergents they contain. Choose a mild soap. In cases of excessive dryness you can even dispense with soap and water washing. A light cleansing gel cleans adequately and also counteracts dryness. Rinse well and then dab with a skin-tonic lotion, preferably one that contains herbal extracts, so that it has a soothing effect. If cotton wool is not appropriate, use a small clean sponge to apply and remove cosmetics. This should be the pre-shave routine.

For your shave, use a cream that is gentle, creamy and emollient. This will soften the hair, making shaving easier, leaving the skin soft and supple. The use of after-shave lotions can also have a drying effect on the skin, because of their alcohol content. Instead, a non-greasy after-shave cream can be used. Sandalwood is an ideal ingredient for after-shave creams, as it has antiseptic properties and a soothing action on the skin. It also has a natural fragrance that is not too over-powering, or decidedly feminine. The cream also helps to keep the skin well moisturised.

Skin protection is a vital part of skin care. The after-shave cream would also form an invisible barrier between the skin and all the factors which cause it to degenerate—like the sun, environmental conditions and pollution. The loss of moisture will be prevented. This will help to delay the formation of lines and wrinkles. The cream, being non-greasy, would be ideal for both oily and dry skins.

If the skin is oily, the cleansing routine should be adjusted. A light cleansing lotion-cum-tonic should be used after washing the face. Spots, pimples and acne may be present, as these conditions are associated with oily skins. If so, a medicated cleanser must be used, in order to reduce surface oil, remove the impurities and heal the condition. Washing the face too often with soap and water would remove the natural acid mantle and leave the skin open to bacterial infections. The skin should be cleansed twice a day. Wipe it with a mild skin tonic as often as required. The skin tonic should have a mild astringent effect and should refresh the skin.

The night care routine for dry and normal skins should include cleansing, followed by a light massage with a nourishing cream. This would help to improve blood circulation, tone the muscles and induce relaxation. Use upward and outward movements while massaging the skin. Wipe off all cream before bedtime. The entire routine should not take more than ten minutes.

A once-a-week facial mask really helps to revitalize the skin. It nourishes and moisturises, apart from helping skin tone and elasticity. Bottled, ready-to-use masks are available. All you need to do is choose one that suits your skin.

The skin reflects the state of our health and the pattern of life we lead. Lack of sleep, unbalanced diets, dietary deficiencies, excess alcohol and smoking are bound to have detrimental effects on the health and the appearance. Beauty is the result of internal health and external care. Yes, this goes for men too!

Grooming the Groom

LOOKING good is not just a woman's prerogative, especially on the "day of all days". It is true that the bride is the apple of all eyes, but this is one occasion when the bride-groom shares a good part of the limelight.

Though most men shy away from any mention of beauty care, they would all agree, I am sure that the knowledge that one is looking one's best, imparts self-confidence.

Self-confidence is one attribute that goes a long way towards projecting the picture of a well-groomed, self-assured man, on his way to taking on the responsibility of a wife and family.

Clothes are definitely a part of good grooming, but that is not all there is to it. Grooming involves the total 'top-to-toe' effect that shows 'care'. It shows that attention has been paid to every detail and it certainly does not detract from masculinity.

Since the wedding date has been set in advance, there should be enough time to pay adequate attention to these details, so that you do not land up with the hangover of last minute hurry, strain and tension.

It is not just that you should look refreshed, but feel it too. Where clothes are concerned, you will, no doubt, go through weeks of choosing, trials and fittings, but be sure to get it over with well in advance to avoid a last minute rush and the possibility of turning up in ill-fitting clothes—it will hardly help your self-confidence.

Since I have spoken of the "top-to-toe" effect, let's start at the top—the hair. If you think you may need a hair cut around the date of the wedding, do not wait till then.

Have your hair cut at least two weeks in advance, so that your hair and style settle by the wedding date. It takes the hair about that time to settle into the style. In any case, your hair will not grow so fast as to need a cut in two weeks' time again.

Besides, you can always have your hair cut after the wedding that is if you don't feel like pulling it out by then!

A hair cut about two weeks before the big day will have another advantage—you will avoid looking like a shorn sheep, even if you feel like a 'lamb to the slaughter'!

The hair should also have a well-conditioned, manageable look and not as if you were caught in a cyclone! There are a number of hair-conditioning products available in the market, which should be used when you shampoo the hair. First, shampoo the hair and rinse it with water. Then apply the conditioner or hair rinse, all over. Wait for a couple of minutes and then rinse the hair well with water.

Rinse it till you think that the hair is cleaned of all grease and soapy residue.

The basic job of a hair-conditioner is to disentangle the hair and make it smooth. It also adds body, life and vitality to the hair. You can also add the white of an egg to the hair about half-an-hour before your shampoo.

Egg white is an excellent cleanser and its protein content also adds body. If there is enough time, you can go in for weekly treatments with henna to impart a healthy, conditioned look to the hair. If your hair tends to be greasy, wash it the day of the wedding. If it is basically dry, have your shampoo a day before.

Like everyday, you will definitely have your shave. But, on this special day, have another one just before you start getting ready—say about an hour before you set out to seal your fate, so that you don't end up with a "six o'clock shadow", just when you want to look freshest and brightest.

And take a great deal of care when you shave, to avoid any nicks and cuts with the razor. Washing your face with hot water prior to applying the shaving cream will help to soften the hair of the beard and make shaving easier. You will also be using an after-shave lotion, like you do everyday. It will help to refresh you and soothe the skin. There are one or two cosmetics you may like to try in advance.

For instance, if your skin is basically dry, an after-shave lotion would cause further dryness. To counteract this effect, you can dab on a light moisturiser after washing the face. If your skin tends to be greasy, use a skin tonic cum astringent to close the pores and tone the skin.

Take a long look at yourself in the mirror. If you find that your eyes look dull and tired, put a few drops of eye lotion. If you have the time and privacy, you can soak cotton wool pads in rose water and put them on the eyes. Lie down and relax for ten minutes. What about a bath? Yes, I know you have one everyday. But this is the big day, isn't it? So take a little more time than usual and give yourself a good scrub.

Pay special attention to the hands and feet, scrubbing the heels with a pumice stone to remove all the dead skin. After your bath, apply talcum powder all over the body, even on the feet.

Perhaps, you can borrow your sister's hand lotion and apply a little on the hands, smoothing it all over, especially at the nails. Wipe off with a moist towel. This will eliminate the effect of soap and water, which make the skin very dry. Actually, a number of men go in for manicures and pedicures these days. So if you can dispel the idea from your mind, that it is a purely feminine pastime, you can have them at a men's parlour the day before the wedding.

Manicured fingers add to the well-groomed look. For one thing the nails will be clean and free of dead skin. A professional pedicure, which includes a foot massage, is very relaxing and you are bound to enjoy it. So, why not give yourself a special treat.

Talking of professional help, why not try a facial? Men's beauty parlours provide this facility as well, though those who avail of it may not want to divulge the secret! For one thing, a professional massage stimulates surface circulation and is a pleasing way to looking good and feeling refreshed. A facial mask, which is part of the facial, helps to cleanse the skin of dead epithelial cells, making the skin cleaner and brighter.

A number of you may suffer from excessive perspiration and if the wedding happens to be in summer, you can take the help of an anti-perspirant.

Anti-perspirants temporarily reduce the delivery of perspiration to the skin surface. Most anti-perspirants are also deodorants and this would serve a dual purpose. You can also wear a vest with sleeves, made of some absorbent material to act as a 'dress sheild'. One word about smelling good. You can use a cologne instead of a perfume, because cologne has a lighter and more subtle fragrance. Choose a good brand because it should stand you in good stead—its going to be a long evening for you.

STORY OF SHAHNAZ HUSAIN

THIS is the story of a Beauty Mogul. Of a woman imbued with a burning desire to recapture India's Great Herbal Heritage. To channelise all her ancient Herbal remedies and cures, incorporating in them the latest advances in Beauty Science.

This is the story of a woman obsessed with a passion for beauty and a vision that knows no bounds. SHAHNAZ HUSAIN, the moving force behind the Shahnaz Herbal range, is, herself a Moghul. The success story of Shahnaz Husain, whose beauty network poses a collosal threat to the synthetic ridden cosmetic world, reads like a fairy tale.

Shahnaz Husain comes from an illustrious family. She is the daughter of Chief Justice N.U. Beg. Her grandfather Mirza Yar Jung was the Chief Justice of Hyderabad and Governor of Nagpur. He was a Moghul who migrated from Samarkhand. Her grandmother's father was Prime Minister of Bhopal and his father was from the ruling Afghan Royal Family. Her mother's father Osman Yar Uddaulah and his father Sir Afsar-ul-Mulk were Commanders-in-Chief in the Hyderabad Army. Shahnaz Husain's uncle M.H. Beg was the Chief Justice of India.

SHAHNAZ HUSAIN is unique to the extent that she is perhaps the only woman in the world to use precious herbal extracts as cures and has an answer to the human need to acquire and preserve beauty. Today, herbs are not a fad, they are an international trend. The natural thought that comes to the minds when we speak of herbs, is India. The West is looking towards us with enlightened eyes. They are sure that nature and herbs are the answer to all the synthetic ills of the West.

When there were no synthetics, India always had herbs. In fact-....whenever you think of synthetics.... you can always find a better answer in nature.

The Shahnaz Herbal range was created as an answer to a human need, the innate desire dormant in every woman to acquire perfection, and to maintain it. In the Shahnaz Herbal chain of salons, each client is handled individually, each skin is diagnosed carefully, classified and then treated according to its individual requirement...Shahnaz Husain herself believes that skin and hair are external barometers of internal body condition. Great accent is placed on diet and general health. A client with problems is put through a series of tests to try and ascertain the basic cause of the condition...unless the inner body health is perfect, cosmetics will only help temporarily. The problem is bound to recur unless the basic cause is treated. Only then can beauty care achieve permanent results.

There is a positive difference between the products made from the extract of the real fruit or herb and the synthetically created extracts. Unless it is the extract of the actual fruit or herb, the God given natural beneficial power of the plant is not there. If the cosmetic contains synthetically created extracts, then the natural beneficial effect is absent.

Most Western countries, in fact, make synthetic. . . natural cosmetics. In India, we use the actual extract of precious herbs. That is why the effect is so remarkable. The unique aspect of the Shahnaz Herbal range, is that it is geared for maintenance and care. What makes the line so special, is that it has been used extensively in helping in the cure of various problems like Alopecia, Falling hair, Dandruff, Acne, Scars, Pigmentation, Blemishes and for minimising the Ageing process.

The most sensational of all of them, the Rosemint—Thermoherb Mask, contains a special thermal herb. It is the same plant which was used in the olden days to indicate the thermal heat of the body when the Moghul Kings had fever.

Shahnaz Herbal is the largest chain of its kind in the world. It is also unique, in the sense that although it crusades the Natural Concept, with ancient herbal remedies, it is constantly incorporating the latest advances in skin science, making it especially acceptable to the Western World.

Since 1977, Shahnaz Husain has regularly appeared on the BBC Television, London, constantly impressing her belief that India must lead the International Cosmetic Empire in Herbal Cosmetics.

She represented India at the New York Beauty Congress in 1978 and at the Monte Carlo World Beauty Congress CIDESCO in 1979. Obsessed with India's image abroad, she has had the rare honour of representing India as President for the Day at the CIDESCO world Congress in New York in 1980 and in Vienna in 1981 and was appointed President of the Congress Proceedings.

Elected Chairman of the I.T.E.C. International Beauty Congress in 1981. . ., she was given a special award by ITEC, U.K., in recognition of her singular efforts in forwarding the cause of Herbal Beauty Therapy in Asia and for being solely responsible for putting India on the World Cosmetic Map.

In July 1981, she represented India at the Cosmetic Fair at Brighton, U.K. She was elected Vice-President, Independent Professional Therapists International, U.K. in January 1982.

In August 1982, Shahnaz Husain became the first Asian to enter the most prestigious Store SELFRIDGES, London to participate in the 'Festival of India'. Shahnaz Herbal Cosmetics were so successful that they airlifted 9 consignments in 10 weeks, breaking a 40-year old British cosmetic sales record, selling a phenomenal 2700 pounds in 2 hours, to the extent that the London Daily headlined the next day... "Herbal Hell Breaks Loose at Selfridges." Shahnaz Herbal now has a permanent counter in Selfridges, London.

In August 1982, a Press conference was held in Munich for her by the famous singer, Mazzie Williams of the BONEY M Group.

In October 1982 she represented India at the Trade Fair in Hong-kong.

In November 1982, she participated in the Trade Fair in London.
In April 1983, she held a Press conference in Kuwait, Doha, Dubai and Abu Dhabi.

In July 1983, she appeared on the BBC, London T V Series "Meet the Herbal Legend" and on the British East-West T V programme entitled, "The Indian Herbal Phenomenon is here"

Shahnaz Husain has been featured by the Indian Government in the Doordarshan Series for the United Nations established consortium, in the U.N. Decade for Women 1983 of Outstanding International Personalities"

Shahnaz Husain represented India at the Beauty Playground Show at Selfridges, London, in February 1984 and spoke during the 'India Hour' on Indian Herbal Cosmetics in the international market.

In July 1984, Shahnaz Husain represented India at the Trade Fair Moscow, USSR, in the State Trading Corporation Pavilion. Fighting for India's rights and recognition on international platforms, she has held Press conferences all over the world. Her success in Moscow had to be seen, to be believed. Twice the chains separating her from the public broke, such was the surge of interested buyers. In fact, she was asked by Russian engineers to stop her herbal make-up demonstrations for fear of roof collapse....

In July 1984, she represented India at the Wembly Beauty Congress, U.K.

In January 1985, Barbara Cartland included the Shahnaz Herbal Line in her personal range of beauty products to be promoted and sold via the Health & Happiness Club.

In April 1985, Shahnaz Husain signed a contract with Saudi Arabia for opening the largest Herbal Centre in Asia and the third largest in the World, in Jeddah, spread over 6 acres with its own 5 Star Hotel to service it. Formerly, Saudi Arabia was inundated with french cosmetics. This is the first time that Saudi Arabia has signed a contract with India for mass marketing herbal cosmetics.

In May 1985, Shahnaz Husain participated in the H.H.E.C. Fabulous Orient Show held at the prestigious store Al Khalijia where she qualified for the Guiness Book of Records by selling 6000 Dinars worth of cosmetics in 2 hours.

In June 1985, Shahnaz Husain held a crowded press conference at the 'Festival of India', Paris and appeared on 'Good Morning Paris'. Herbs, nature and India are in a very big way in France. It is for the first time in the cosmetic history of Paris that the French have signed a contract with India for cosmetics. The opening of Shahnaz Herbal at the Sona shop in Paris was a historical event.

In July 1985, Shahnaz Husain was in the USA to attend the Festival of India and introduced her herbal cosmetics in the Smithsontan Museum Shop, recording phenomenal sales. She also opened a Cosmetic Shop at the prestigious store BLOOMINGDALE'S in New York in April 1986, once more becoming the first Asian to sell cosmetics in the USA.

In June 1986, Shahnaz Husain appeared on ABC T V, New York and on the "New York Cafe Live"

In October 1986, Shahnaz Husain held a crowded press conference at the Indian High Commission in New York with a Herbal Demonstration which was televised nation-wide and heavily covered.

In November 1986, Shahnaz Husain held a press conference at India House, London, speaking of India in the world in herbal cosmetics. Shahnaz Husain is the first Asian to enter the fastidious British Market in herbal cosmetics.

Covered by 81 International, 345 Indian newspapers and with 8390 articles to her credit, she probably receives one of the widest press coverages in the world. She contributes to 19 Indian newspapers and 11 abroad. It would be difficult to name a newspaper or magazine that has not written of her crusade for natural herbal aids.

The company she heads is not a faceless brand promoter...Shahnaz Herbal has a charismatic woman and a beautiful story behind it. The story of a woman who has dedicated her life to making other people's life more beautiful. For hundreds of women all over the world...she has made life worth living and the world a lovelier place to be in. Her's is a range with a dynamic woman to propel it and with a history behind it...of India's vast and rich herbal heritage, encompassing a centuries old civilization, yet always ready to absorb the latest scientific knowledge. Shahnaz Husain's Beauty Institute, Woman's World International, attracts students from several countries. Like a Mecca of knowledge, they converge upon this shrine of learning from all over the World.

Shahnaz Husain has over 100 franchise clinics in India and abroad. She personally flies in for the opening of her clinics, attends press conferences speaks to the crowds in the area, telling them of the ill effects of synthetics and the curative powers of herbs, prescribes natural remedies to as many clients as possible and is often back home on the same day. The crowds that swarm to meet her on her flying visits have to be seen, to be believed. She has brought a new meaning to the word 'Beauty' and Shahnaz Herbal is a magnificient expression of her dreams, hopes and aspirations.

Shahnaz Husain, heading the largest herbal chain of its kind in the world....has become a legend in her own lifetime.

Awards Recognition
Received by Shahnaz Husain

1) In May 1984, Shahnaz Husain was presented the 'WOMAN OF THE YEAR 1984'—UDYOG RATTAN AWARD, by the President of India—Shri Giani Zail Singh, for excellence in export performance and being solely responsible for putting India on the World Cosmetic Map.

2) In January 1985, Shahnaz Husain was given the Silver Award for the 'BEST WOMAN ENTREPRENEUR', by the Vice-President of India—Shri R.Venkataraman.

3) In May 1985, Shahnaz Husain was awarded the 'IMAGE INDIA AWARD '85' by Shri K.A. Khan, Minister of External Affairs—at a glittering function for promoting the image of India abroad.

4) In August 1985, Shahnaz Husain was awarded the 'IBC WOMAN OF THE YEAR 1985',—as the outstanding personality of the year in the Decade of Women. She was given the SHIROMANI AWARD for Kala Saudariya, by Shri Vasant Sathe, Cabinet Minister of Steel.

5) In March 1986, Shahnaz Husain was awarded the 'FICCI AWARDS 1985' by Shri Abid Husain, Member Planning Commission, for outstanding Woman Entrepreneur and for promoting the image of India and its herbal heritage abroad.

6) In July 1986, Shahnaz Husain was presented the 'UDYOG RATTAN AWARD 1986' by the President of India, Shri Giani Zail Singh, for outstanding performance in promotion of Indian Herbal Cosmetics in the international market.

7) In July 1986, Shahnaz Husain also received the most prestigious IES 'WOMAN OF THE YEAR AWARD' from Shri V.N. Gadgil, Minister of Information & Broadcasting, for excellent export performance of Indian Herbal Cosmetics.

8) Shahnaz Husain received the ITEC 'FLYING FALCON AWARD' in December 1986.

Woman's World International Beauty Institute

SHAHNAZ HUSAIN sincerely believes, that regardless of her status in life before or after marriage, every woman must be economically independent. For this, a Diploma or Technical qualification is a necessity, preferably before marriage, to equip her to face the unknown future with confidence. With this in mind she opened the Woman's World International Beauty Institute.

For girls who are seriously interested in beauty culture as a career, the Institute offers many advantages over apprenticeship training. In a busy salon, no matter how competent the staff may be, there is little time and less opportunity to explain the scientific principles on which all good beauty treatment is based today, and without such instructions the learner cannot hope to become proficient.

The Beauty Institute gives theoretical instructions concurrently with Video classes and practical demonstrations. There is ample scope for individuals to practice on live models. This is the only Beauty Institute in Asia which is affiliated with the International Therapy Examination Centre (I.T.E.C.), London, U.K. Students qualifying from here can work anywhere in the world. She herself completed the Teacher's Training Course at I.T.E.C. London, U.K.

It is also affiliated to the Christine Valmy School of Beauty, New York, which allows a Woman's World International Diploma Holder and a Post-Graduate student to study at the Christine Valmy School, Fifth Avenue, for 40 hours in Aesthetics and appear for their examination. The Valmy International School is accredited and approved by the University of the State of New York.

Woman's World International is also affiliated to:—

1. International Beauty Academy—Sydney, Australia.
2. School of Cosmetology—Vancouver, Canada.
3. Clara International Beauty Therapy Academy—Kuala Lumpur, Malaysia.
4. Monita Beauty School—Hongkong
5. International Beauty Centre—Athens, Greece.
6. International Therapy Examination Centre, London, U.K.
7. Christine Valmy, New York, U.S.A.
8. Park School of Beauty, U.K.

There are no fixed hours. The school runs non-stop from 9 a.m. to 4 p.m. Students are expected to put in their attendance for the number of hours prescribed. This is a British system to facilitate students, career women and housewives joining. Therefore working outstation girls or college students can put in a few hours off and on and still sit for a regular Diploma examination at the end of 200 hours.

Woman's World International also has a free Deaf & Dumb Institute called 'SHAMUTE INTERNATIONAL' to give free technical education for Deaf & Dumb girls to make them into career beauticians

RANGE OF PRODUCTS

Range of Creams

SHAZEMA : *Greaseless Medicated Cream Soap*

A complete beauty programme for a smoother, softer complexion. Removes dirt, oil and make-up, yet does not make the skin dry as ordinary soap does. Effective for sunburnt/chapped skins. A rare moisturised deep cleansing treatment for oily/dry skins. Leaves a moisture film on the skin.

Method of Use : Scoop out *Shazema* and apply on face, neck and hands. Work gently in circular motion—like a soap. Rinse off. Avoid eye area.

SHASMOOTH : *Almond Lanolin—Under Eye Cream*

Helps remove dark circles around the eyes. The pure almond oil and lanolin, used in this preparation, nourish and clear the skin. The potato extract contained in it, with Vitamins A & D and other herbal ingredients reinforce the anti-wrinkle properties.

Method of Use : Apply around the eyes. Leave for 5 minutes. Use sparingly. Remove gently with moist cotton wool.

Note : Must not be left overnight. If sensitive to lanolin, discontinue use.

SHALIFE : *Vitaminised Nourishing Cream*

This is a luxurious night cream, providing your skin with a meaningful, vitaminised, built-in moisturising system. Rapidly absorbed, it gives the skin all it needs, without being unnecessarily greasy. The combination of wheatgerm oil, cabbage and date extracts perform the dual purpose of softening and nourishing. The Vitamin E, it contains, has the capacity of accelerating the healing of scar tissue, improving spotty skin, thus restoring collagen elasticity.

Method of Use : Massage into skin gently using upward strokes, at bedtime. Leave on for 5 minutes. Remove with moist cotton wool.

SHACLEANSE : *Cactus Aloe Vera Rehydrant Cleansing Cream*

A powerful rehydrant cleansing cream which removes impurities from the skin's surface without disturbing its moisture balance. Aloe Vera, known as "The Desert Lily" has a powerful water retention quality and acts as an effective moisturiser. The natural extracts of lemon, carrot and other herbal extracts contained in the product have antiseptic and germicidal properties.

Method of Use : Apply on face, neck and hands. Gently massage in circular movements. Remove with moist cotton wool. Excellent for normal to dry skin.

SHASILK : *Vanishing Rose—All Purpose Cream*

This light frothy cream has a nonoily base and can be used any time anywhere as a softening cream. The natural extract of dates used in this cream acts as an effective antiwrinkle moisturiser. This emollient cream provides an invisible film of moisture which protects the skin from the hazards of environmental pollution.

Method of Use: Excellent as a total protective coverage for the skin. Its use in combination with (Sandalwood Protective Base) *Shabase* is recommended for normal to oily skin, guarding against moisture loss and air pollution.

SHADEW : *Dew Drops—Turmeric Pre-wash Cream*

This has the capacity of protecting the skin from the chlorinating and ageing effect of water. The turmeric in the cream has a mild depilatory action on superfluous hair, suppressing growth. The carrot extract and lemon oil mixed in this cream nourish the skin with natural vitamins and works as an effective antiseptic and anti-freckle agent.

Method of Use

Apply all over the face, neck and hands. Wash off. Protects the skin from the ageing effect of water. Gives a satin smooth effect.

SHAFAIR : *Vitaminished Whitening Cream*

It is a safe and effective preparation specially created for lightening the skin colour. Free from all the harmful ingredients which are usually present in such preparations. It may be used once or twice a day. It contains pure almond oil, lactic acid, Vitamins A & D and carrot seed extract.

Method of Use: Clean scar mark or pigmented patch with (Skin Tonic) *Sharose* with moist cotton wool. Apply on problem area in the afternoon or evening. Leave on.

Note : Do not expose face to the sun. Avoid application near eyes. If sensitivity occurs, discontinue use.

SHAGLOSS : *Deep Cleanser Ginseng*

This is a complex of biologically powerful effective natural herbs, Ginseng extract, arnica and ashwagandha extracts, enriched with natural Vitamins A & D.

Method of Use : Excellent for removing make-up. After application remove with moist cotton wool. Good for reconditioning very dry cracked feet.

SHABASE : *Hide-n-Heal— Sandalwood Protective Base*

An ideal all-purpose antiseptic total coverage, reinforced with pure sandalwood oil acting as a protective base. Created specially for sensitive and problem skins, it acts as a heal and conceal base. It protects the skin from the harmful effects of the sun's rays. The honey reinforces the natural moisture content, with anti-pollution qualities of sandalwood.

Method of Use: Can be used morning and evening. In combination with *Shasilk*, its use is recommended for normal to oily skin and with *Shaglow* for normal to dry skin. A miraculous beauty formula with immense pore-porcelaining powers, takes on the natural colour of the skin—being transparent in quality. Can be used several times a day.,

SHABLEM : *Blemish Ointment*

A specially effective, clinically tested ointment for skin blemishes, scars and freckles. Used regularly, will make the skin lighter, smoother and healthier.

Method of Use : Rub into scars, pigmented spots or freckles at bedtime. Leave on all night. If irritation occurs, discontinue use. Wipe off preferably with (Clear-It) *Shamint* next morning.

SHADERM : *Anti-rash Cream*
A clinically tested, medicated protective barrier cream for control of irritant dermatitis, rash and problem skin. Protects skin from atmospheric pollution.

Method of Use : Application in combination with *Shaclove* is recommended for rash, irritated skin or acne. Apply all over the affected areas for about 20 minutes. Let it dry and wash off. Can be used any time of the day.

SHABRIGHT : *Anti-tan*
Extremely effective for tanned, scarred pigmented, blemished area, to be used sparingly after skin test.

Method of Use : Apply a little on the upper arm area, leave on for 15 minutes. (This is a patch test). If no irritation occurs, then apply with finger tips on the tanned, scarred, pigmented, blemished area, avoiding eyes. Use sparingly. Avoid sun after use.

SHAPEACH : *Apricot Lustre— Firming Cream*
Pure apricot extract, in this preparation acts as a powerful astringent, porcelains the skin and contracts the pores. Vitamins A and D and other herbal extracts present in the cream give lustre to dry and dull skin. Rose oil acts as a beautifying agent. Excellent as a neck, hand and body treatment.

Method of Use : Apply on the neck, arms and body. Is excellent as a hand and neck cream. Can be massaged in gently after bath on the body/bust as a firming cream—can be used effectively on stretch mark area after bath.

SHAGLOW : *Honey Intensive*
The honey it contains is a natural and effective moisturiser and acts as an excellent softening agent, giving maximum nourishment to the skin. It also contains pure sandalwood oil and other herbal extracts with skin beautifying properties.

Method of Use : For dry skin. Apply after cleaning the face. Its use in combination with (Hide-n-Heal) *Shabase* is recommended for normal to dry skin. Excellent as a total protective coverage, guarding the skin against moisture loss and air pollution.

SHAQUEEN : *Precious Herb*
Used by ancient fabled Moghul Queens to moisturise their skins, it is enriched with valuable herbs like tulsi (basil), wild turmeric, date and apricot. The value of tulsi is known for its youth giving powers and has been used for generations in the ancient Indian system of medicine— Ayurveda, for maintaining skin elasticity and giving it a porcelain look. Light in texture, the cream is readily absorbed leaving a fine— invisible moisture film. Excellent under make-up.

Method of Use : Apply sparingly all over the face and neck in a thin film. Use as required.

SHAFLIGHT : *Air Travel Sandalwood Moisturiser*
Made from precious herbs, it is a non-greasy cream moisturiser specially developed to control dehydration and dryness during air travel. Enriched with extracts of date, carrot, sunflower seeds, honey, seashell, sandalwood and almond oil. Keeps skin supple smooth and soft, especially during flights.

Method of Use : Suits all skin types. Apply on the face, neck and hands, can be used under make-up which helps you to travel beautifully.

BARBARA CARTLAND HONEY : *Rose, Mint, Moisture Plus*

A powerful moisturiser enriched with extracts of sacred basil, mint, honey, rose and sandalwood oil. Ideal for all skin types. Helps porcelain the skin and acts as an effective moisture trap sealing in natural moisture with an invisible shield.

Method of Use : Can be used sparingly, once or twice a day.

SHAMILK : *Under-Eye Day Lotion*

An effective under eye lotion enriched with sandalwood and almond oil, Vitamin A and D from natural sources.

Method of Use : Apply during the day and allow the lotion to act for about 15 to 20 minutes. Remove with *Shawipe*. An excellent rejuvenation programme for exhausted eyes.

SHAWIPE : *Lemon, Tulsi Herbal Skin Freshner.*

Excellent for refreshing tired exhausted skin. Can be used several times a day as a moisture based cleanser, and instant skin pick-up.

Method of Use : Use like a moist cleanser. Keep in refrigerator for maximum benefit in summer for the cool fresh feeling.

SHATAJ

A combination of wild lily, rose and tulsi, was used by ancient Moghul. Queens to moisturise their fabled skins. Enriched with precious herbs, it acts as a powerful moisturiser. The value of tulsi is known for its youth giving powers and has been used for generations in the ancient Ayurvedic system of medicine for maintaining skin ellasticity and giving the skin a porcelain, youthful look. Excellent all purpose moisture cream.

Method of Use : Apply. Leave on. For all skin types.

SHAMEN : *Cream for Men*

Enriched with neem bark, menthol, precious herbs, and pure sandalwood oil. It protects the skin against over exposure to sun and wind. It is antiseptic moisturising and emollient. Excellent as an effective after shave cream, especially to help heal cuts and irritants resulting from shaving.

Method of Use : Wash face with *Shazema*. Apply *Shamen* all over face and neck. Can be used several times a day.

Range of Lotions

SAHMOIST : *Date Enriched Moisture Milk*

One of the most flexible moisturising treatments ever invented. An all-purpose natural moisturiser, reinforced with apricot, date, wild flowers and other herbal extracts. Can be used day or night as an effective 'moisture trap', sealing in natural moisture with an invisible shield. Guards against moisture loss, while letting the skin breathe. Helps make the skin smoother, fresher, softer.

Method of Use : Apply all over the face, neck and arms in the same way as a normal moisturiser. Excellent for any type of skin. Can be used under make-up giving the skin a moisturised surface to help make-up last longer. Can be used in combination with *Shabase* to protect the skin against pollution/providing total coverage.

SHABATH : *Body Satin Sandalwood Shampoo*

This body shampoo is rich in pure Sandalwood oil. The precious wood has been known for generations for its youth giving natural antiseptic properties. Gentle on the skin, it leaves the body sparkling and satin smooth, without disturbing the natural acid mantle of the skin. Ideal for counter-acting the ageing and chlorinating effect of water on the body. Excellent for use after swimming or at the seaside.

Method of Use : Pour 4 tsp. or more of body shampoo into the bath tub for the foamy effect. Soak for 15 minutes. Shower off.

SHAMINT : *Clear-it*

A powerful deep cleansing lotion especially prepared to protect the skin from the hazards of atmospheric pollution. This antiseptic preparation clears the skin of embedded impurities and micro organisms. Regular use, even for normal skin as a pre-make-up protective lotion is recommended.

Method of Use : Use cotton wool to apply all over the affected acne areas once or twice a day, avoiding the eyes. Wipe off gently with dry cotton wool after 20 minutes. Can be left, overnight. Ideal as a gentle soothing agent for cleaning the skin.

SHAFLOWER : *After Bath Body Lotion*

Rich in herbal oils and extracts such as aloe vera, curcuma aromatica, sandalwood oil, ashwagandha, rajnigandha and other precious herbal extracts and skin softners. This rejuvenating body lotion is light in texture and readily absorbed by the skin so as to leave the body moisturised and porcelain. Natural water washes away a large amount of the acid mantle of the skin, thereby accelerating the ageing process. *Shaflower* used as an after bath body lotion leaves an invisible film of moisture on the skin and induces rehydration of the statum corneum. A luxurious formulation which cleanses and softens.

SHAROSE : *Rose Skin Tonic*

The natural extracts of dates, mint, cabbage and other herbal ingredients contained in this formula work as a powerful skin texturiser, toner/moisturiser. Controls dehydration and tightens pores. Leaves skin vibrant and petal-soft.

Method of Use : Use with moist cotton wool. Dab like a toner on face. Can also be used as a non-oily cleanser to remove superficial impurities and to refresh the skin. May be used several times a day. Can be used effectively for blackheads in combination with *Shagrain.*

SHACLEAR : *Skin Clear Anti-pimple Lotion*

A clinically tested and extremely effective lotion prepared to help acne, pimples and skin blemishes. Use cotton wool to apply all over the affected areas once or twice a day, avoiding eyes. Can be left overnight. A miracle formula.

Method of Use : Shake bottle well. Apply with cotton wool on the affected areas once or twice a day, avoiding eyes. If sensitivity occurs, discontinue use.

SHABLEACH : *Aqua Bleach*

A powerful skin lightener with the unique combination of carrot seed extract. Helps to remove scars, freckles and minor skin blemishes.

Method of Use : Mix 4 tsp. *Shaface,* 2 tsp. *Shafresh,* 5 drops *Shableach,*

1 tsp. honey, 1 egg (if oily use egg white, if dry add egg yolk), 1 tsp. yoghurt. Mixed and can be kept in fridge for 1 week. Apply, let dry, wash off. If the paste hardens due to moisture evaporation add milk or yoghurt to soften. Can be used every day on oily or dry skin. A rare skin care programme. If sensitivity occurs, discontinue use.

SHAFRESH : *Seaweed Lotion*
An effective combination of pure honey, extracts of aloe, seaweed and other herbs, which contain natural moisturising germicidal and anti-wrinkle qualities. Maintains the acid mantle of the skin.
Method of Use : Seaweed lotion can be applied on the face by itself, several times a day, especially before applying any cream or make-up. Can be used with *Shaface.*

SHAHERB : *Body Massage Oil*
Blended with rare vegetable oils and skin vitamins. This precious oil gives your body a satin smooth youthful look. Gentle massage daily with *Shaherb* will help tone skin texture, maintaining the smooth vibrant look.
Method of Use : Apply on body in firm circular movements. Wash off. Excellent for use at the sea-side, will control the ageing dehydrating effect of the salt/sea-water on the body.

SHAWHITE : *Pigmentation Lotion*
A natural de-pigmenting treatment with a rare blend of herbal extracts, created to remove skin blemishes and pigmentation. Helps to maintain the natural acid mantle of the skin. Avoid application near the eyes, lips and hair.
Method of Use : Clean area with (Skin Tonic) *Sharose.* Apply pig-

mentation lotion in the morning with moist cotton wool on scar patch, or pigmented area. Avoid eyes. If sensitivity occurs, discontinue use.

SHAMOON : *Sandalwood Cleansing Milk*
An exceptionally light milk to ensure cleansing of oily/clogged skin. It nourishes the pores with precious herbal extracts of nutmeg and dill seeds leaving skin porcelain smooth.
Method of Use : Apply on face and neck in light circular finger movements. Wash off or remove with moist cotton wool.

Range of Masks
SHAFACE : *Herbal Facial Skin Conditioner*
This is a powerful herbal powder, enriched with sandalwood, almond powder, henna and various herbal extracts. It provides a deep cleansing treatment giving sheen and lustre to the skin and tightening the pores, thus removing wrinkles and blemishes. Its use in combination with egg, milk, honey, seaweed and aqua bleach is recommended. The paste is applied all over the face and neck (avoiding the eyes), left on to dry and washed off. Excellent as an anti-scar, anti-blemish agent and miraculous for porcelaining pores and dermabrasing scars and wrinkles.
Method of Use : An ideal herbal home skin conditioner for open pores, scars, pigmentation, freckles, wrinkles, tanned, dehydrated or problem skins. Mix 4 tsp. *Shaface*, 2 tsp. *Shafresh*, 5 drops *Shableach*, 1 tsp. honey, 1 egg (if oily use egg white, if dry add egg yolk), 1 tsp. yoghurt. Mixed and can be kept in fridge for 1 week. Apply, let dry,

wash off. If the paste hardens due to moisture evaporation add milk or yoghurt to soften. Can be used everyday on oily or dry skin. A rare skin care programme. If sensitivity occurs, discontinue use. Wash off preferably with milk and then water. If skin is sensitive use *Shamint* instead of *Shableach.*

SHAWEEDS : *Seaweed Mask— Rehydrant Skin Treatment*
An all-purpose revitalising, relaxing and refreshing mask. The gentle, soothing action of seaweed mask will help your face regain· the smooth, healthy-appearance of a youthful skin. It contains rare constituents, including seaweed extract, which has an extremely beneficial action on dull, dehydrated skins, rehydrating the delicate tissues surrounding the eyes. It helps the facial muscles to relax and makes expression lines less pronounced. A total moisture treatment in itself.
Method of Use : Apply evenly on the face and neck, including the area surrounding the eyes. Let dry. Wash off. It is effective for sunburnt, chapped/dry skins. A moistured deep cleansing treatment for oil-dry skins. Avoid getting mask into the eyes.

SHAYOUTH : *Placentaherb Mask*
A specially developed mask with placenta and precious herbal extracts, particularly good for revitalising skin, tightening pores and giving it a flawless, satin smooth look. Created especially to counteract the ill-effects of sun and air pollution.
Method of Use : Should be applied all over the face, neck and hands. Let dry and wash off. Avoid eye area. Can be used everyday.

SHATEX : *Protein Mask*
A texturising and nourishing mask enriched with whole egg powder and precious herbs. It helps to erase lines and scars. Tightens pores.
Method of Use : Apply all over the face and neck avoiding eye area. Allow it to dry. Wash off preferably with milk and then water.

SHAMASK-I : *Reviva Face Mask*
An anti-wrinkle balm, reinforced with bael, tolu, balsam, sandalwood oil, date extract, honey and other herbal extracts, helps to porcelain skin and tighten pores.
Method of Use : Apply pack on the face and neck. Avoid eye area. Let dry. Wash off preferably with milk first and then water. Can be used daily. Excellent for improving skin quality.

SHAMASK-2 : *Bust Firming Pack*
An effective herbal body pack, especially created for bust/body firming.
Method of Use : Apply on as desired. Let dry and wash off. Created for body firming. Can be used daily. Effective in lightening stretch marks.

SHAPEEL : *Apricot Honey Peel- off Mask Reinforced with Honey and Bael*
An effective and powerful blend of pure honey, extract of apricot and other herbal oils, which tighten pores, nourishes skin making it lustrous and youthful. The moisture mask lifts impurities effectively leaving the skin tight and refreshed. Excellent for conditioning hands and acts as an effective treatment for controlling facial hair and lightening stretch marks.
Method of Use : Clean face with moist cotton wool and *Sharose.*

Apply a fine layer on the skin, avoid eye area. Be careful the mask does not drip. Let dry for 20 minutes, peel-off gently.

SHACLOVE : *Face Treatment*

Especially developed for oily, rash and acne sensitive conditions. It smoothens and beautifies the skin. Can be applied twice a day, over the affected area or all over the face, avoiding the eye area. Let dry and wash off.

Method of Use : Application in combination with *Shaderm* is recommended for acne, rash or irritated skin. Can be used as a home skin care programme. Clean the face with (Skin Tonic) *Sharose* on moist cotton wool. Smooth on fine film of *Shaclove*. Leave on for 20 minutes. Wash off with milk then water. Ideal for all kinds of skin. Excellent as a pre-party instant pick-up mask.

Range of Hair Care

SHANEL : *Herbal Hair Rinse*

A rare combination of mint, brahmi and other herbal extracts. It deep cleanses the scalp, while maintaining its natural acid mantle. An effective control for dandruff and scalp disorders. Promotes hair growth. Used in combination with henna/amla shampoo offers miraculous results.

Method of Use : Use in combination with *Shamla* for normal to dry hair or *Shahenna* for normal to oily hair. Can be used by itself also. Acts as a powerful anti-dandruff treatment. Wash off with herbal shampoo.

SHACARE : *Herbal Hair Conditioner*

This is a powerful combination of invaluable herbal ingredients like amla. sandalwood, brahmi, lichens and other precious herbs. A complete hair food treatment. Makes the hair strong, healthy and lustrous. Prevents hair loss and acts as a deep scalp cleanser, while maintaining the natural moisture balance. Excellent for giving body to dull, lifeless hair.

Method of Use : Does not colour or discolour the hair. Mix approximately 2 teacups of *Shacare* with 2 raw eggs, 4 tsp. each of coffee powder and lime juice and ½ cup yoghurt. Apply all over scalp and hair. Let dry for 1 hour. Wash off. If hair is oily, avoid yoghurt. Add more eggs for ideal paste.

SHALISMA : *Herbal Mint/Hair Gloss Conditioner*

It is used as a hair sheen. Apply very little on the palms of your hands and rub on hair to give lustre and gloss. Can also be used just before shampoo, massaged into the scalp, left on, and shampooed later. An excellent texturiser. Can be used thrice a week as a hair conditioner.

SHALOCKS : *Herbal Hair Oil*

An effective combination of arnica, henna, shikakai and other herbal extracts, especially created to prevent hair loss and promote luxurious hair growth. An invaluable hair-oil treatment.

Method of Use : To be applied on scalp night before washing. Apply with cotton wool.

SHAHAIR : *Herbal Henna— Reinforced Hair Food Treatment*

Pure henna leaves with a number of herbal ingredients used in this preparation, make the hair lustrous manageable and silky. It also works as a powerful treatment for scalp disorders. Gives a mild natural colour and sheen to the hair.

Method of Use: Mix, depending on the length of the hair, quantity of henna powder and enough raw eggs to make powder into smooth paste consisting of 4 tsp. each of coffee powder and lime juice and ½ cup yoghurt. Do not add water at all. Apply all over scalp and hair. Let dry for about 1 hour. Wash off. It may give a reddish tinge to the hair. If hair is oily, avoid yoghurt. If hair is brittle or dry, add 2 tsp. *Shalocks.* Washing hair with *Shahenna* is recommended. If colour is desired avoid yoghurt, leave on for 2 hours. Excellent for giving highlights to dull lifeless hair.

SHAHENNA : *Herbal Henna Shampoo-For normal to Oily Hair*
A unique blend of henna and other herbal extracts to cleanse the scalp. Controls excessive secretion of scalp oil and imparts sheen to dull hair making it tangle-free. A hair treatment in itself.

Method of Use: Does not colour or discolour the hair. Is excellent for normal to oily hair. Use in combination with *Shanel* (Hair Rinse) for luxuriant hair, controlling hair falling, dandruff and guarding the scalp against infection. Protects the natural acid mantle of the scalp.

SHATONE : *Herbal Hair Tonic*
A miracle formula for controlling hair loss/dandruff/ greying hair. Stimulates hair growth and thickness. A specialised tonic treatment for revitalising the hair and generating a natural lustrous glow. Excellent for texturising rough, brittle hair and split ends.

Method of Use : Apply directly on scalp, preferably every morning with cotton wool. Gently massage in circular movements with finger tips for a few seconds and leave on. No need to wash. It will evaporate, as it is only non-oily. Will give life, body and nourishment to the hair.
Note : In case of any allergic reaction, discontiue use.

SHAMLA : *Herbal Amla Shampoo—for Normal to Dry Hair*
Extracts of amla, dates, arnica and other rare herbs contained in this shampoo, make the hair lustrous, healthier and manageable. Cleanses the scalp while retaining and stimulating its natural oils.

Method of Use: Recommended for normal to oily hair. In combination with *Shanel* (Hair Rinse) is recommended for luxuriant hair, to guard the scalp against infection and to control hair whitening and accelerate growth.

Range of Make-ups
SHASHINE : *Floral Lip Gloss*
A rare blend of herbal extracts and emollients such as calamus, curcula aromatica, almond, glycyrrhiza, saffron, sandalwood oil, marigold and other precious herbal ingredients to smoothen and protect the lips from chapping and discolouration thereby improving skin quality. Can be used alone or on top of lipstick. Shades— 1) Wild Rose 2) Saffron 3) Almond

SHALINE : *Neem Eyeliner*
This is a specially developed herbal liner containing precious herbal ingredients such as phyllanthes, terminalia chebula, almond, neem, camphor and castor oil. Prevents

the drying/flaking effect of normal eyeliners because of its natural herbal ingredients and the almond content.

SHABRIDE : *Floral Sindur*

Now for the first time a scientifically developed safe herbal sindur containing invaluable herbs and flowers such as hibiscus, marigold, sunflower, babtachandan and others. It is free from harmful ingredients that are generally associated with hair loss. Shade—hibiscus red.

SHA-EYES : *Herbal Eye Glamour*

A very special combination of herbs and pure almond oil to pamper your eyes. Makes eyes look exotic and healthy. The content of trifala in this product helps to improve eye sight, while the pure almond oil encourages the growth of luxuriant lashes. Can be easily removed with the help of cactus-aloe cleansing cream.

Method of Use : Can be used daily. In case of irritation due to sensitivity, discontinue use. Can be easily removed with *Shacleanse* (Cactus Aloe) cleanser and moist cotton wool. The almond content encourages growth of luxuriant lashes, and reconditions the skin surrounding the eyes while trifala sharpens the vision.

SHALIPS : *Floral Lipstick*

A combination of precious herbal oils including sandalwood oil, calamus, aloe vera, carrot seed, wheatgerm, ashwagandha and hibiscus to soften and protect the lips, making them look glamorous and act as a moisture treatment as well. Shades—1) Ruby Red 2) Flame Orage 3) Coffee Caramel 4) Nut Brown 5) Jaipur Pink.

Miscellaneous

SHADUST : *Perfumed Floral Talc*

A scientifically blended body talc containing precious ingredients such as sandalwood and ashwagandha that gives the body a satin smooth effect. Its herbal perfume leaves the body refreshed.

SHAGRAIN : *Herbal Beauty Grains*

It is used in combination with skin scars and freckles, blemishes and blackheads. It is enriched with vitamins and rare herbal ingredients to smoothen and beautify the skin. Excellent for treatment of open pores. Has a depilatory action on facial hair. Make a paste by mixing with skin tonic *Sharose*.

Method of Use : It's use in combination with (Skin Tonic) *Sharose* is recommended. Take a small amount of *Shagrain* on the palm of your hand, mix with *Sharose* and apply on oily, pigmented, scarred and blackhead areas gently in circular movements. Avoid rubbing into acne or pimples. Wash off.

VEGETABLE PEELING

The treatment is given for scars (acne, smallpox, injuries, birth marks, burns) pigmentation, open pores, sagging skin, stretch marks, wrinkles etc. It is not to be given if there are pimples and acne, but can be used after the condition subsides. Excellent for dermabrasing premature wrinkles.

THERMOHERB MASK

The thermoherb mask is based on an ancient thermal mask, which has been improved by modern cosmetology and has now been perfected by the substitution of herbal extracts. The Thermoherb Mask contains natural extracts of herbs like rose, bael, mint and henna. The mask also has the capacity of generating heat up to 40°C, which creates an ideal condition for cream absorbtion. The heat increases blood circulation and as the mask cools down and hardens, it tightens pores and tissues, sculpting the jaw line and even double chins, minimising wrinkles,improving muscle tone and skin elasticity. The thermoherb mask is not only one of the latest developments in skin beauty, but is a complete treatment, in fact, it is an instant mini face-lift. The results have to be seen and believed.

SHASCENT : *Flora Cream Sachet*
A cream sachet with an exotic earthy scent and a distinct herbal note. The lingering perfume is rich in sandalwood and invaluable precious herbs.

SHACLEAN : *Herbal Toothpaste*
A number of proven herbs such as walnut, neem, babul, trifala, akkal kadha, clove and mint. A new formulation of herbs taking total care

of dental hygiene, leaving teeth sparkling and fresh. Use daily morning and night. Can also be used as a mouth wash after meals, diluted in a mug of water.

Method of Use : Use after meals, also at morning and night Use tooth brush if desired.

SHAHNAZ HERBAL RANGE OF MEN

Skin Care	*Hair Care*
1. Shalisma	1. Shamla
2. Shaglow	2. Shahenna
3. Shasilk	3. Shaherb
4. Shabase	4. Shalocks
5. Shazema	5. Shatone
6. Shaoint	6. Shanel
7. Shamen	

Note : As in synthetics there can be a reaction—so also, in herbs which are natural or organic, there can be a harmless reaction. Because the products are purely herbal, it is not possible to guarantee colour and consistency from batch to batch. Our dependence on nature does not lessen the efficacy of the products.

GLOSSARY

HINDI NAME	ENGLISH NAME	BOTANICAL NAME
1. Amla	Amla	Phyllanthes emblica
2. Bael	Bael	Aegle marmelos
3. Ashwagandha	Winter Cherry	Withania somnifera
4. Brahmi	Centella	Centella asiatica
5. Pudina	Mint	Mentha arvensis
6. Behada	Baleric myrobalans	Terminalia balerica
7. Harda	Chebulic myrobalans	Terminalia chebula
8. Haldi	Turmeric	Curcuma longa
9. Lavang	Clove	Caryophyllus aromaticus
10. Arnica	Arnica	Premna integrifolia
11. Mehndi	Henna	Lausonia alba
12. Nilgiri	Eucalyptus	Eucalyptus globulus
13. Khajur	Dates	Phoenix dactylefera
14. Gobhi	Cabbage	Brassica oleracea
15. Amba haldi	Wild turmeric	Curcuma aromatica
16. Adrak	Ginger	Zingiber Orrensis
17. Akrod	Walnut	Juglans regia
18. Mulethi	Licquorice	Glycerrhiza glabra
19. Kabab Chini	Cubebs	Cubeba officinalis
20. Neem	Margosa	Melia azadarachta
21. Badam	Almond	Prunus amygdalys
22. Gunj	Jequirity	Abrus precatorius
23. Chini ghas	Seaweed	Gelidium cartilageum
24. Shikakai	Shikakai	Acacia concinna
25. Chhadila	Lichens	Parmelia perlata
26. Khumani	Apricot	Prunus armeniaca
27. Bach	Calamus	Acorus calamus
28. Tesu	Butea	Butea frondosa
29. Genda	Marigold	Tagetes erecta
30. Ghikanwar	Aloe	Aloevera, Aloe indica
31. Gajar	Carrot	Daucus carota
32. Parijat	Nyctanthes	Nycthanthes arbor-tristis
33. Gulab	Rose	Roda damascena
34. Rajnigandha	Rajnigandha	Polianthes tuberosa
35. Kesar	Saffron	Crocus sativus
36. Chandan	Sandalwood	Santalum album
37. Raktachandan	Red sandalwood	Pterocarpus santalinus
38. Dalchini	Cinnamon	Cinnamomum cassia
39. Ratan Jot	Alkanet root	Onosma echioides
40. Gienseng	Ginseng	—
41. Tolu Balsam	Tolu Balsam	—
42. Shahed	Honey	—
43. Sowa	Dill	Peucedanum graveolens
44. Ajowan	Ajowan	Carum copticum
45. Jaiphal	Nutmeg	Myristica fragrans

Copies of this book are also available at :

Head Office , Salon
M-86, Greater Kailash-I
New Delhi-110 048
Tel : 643 9434, 641 4981
Telex : 31-71382 SHAH IN
Fax : 91-11-6463903

Branches :

- M-84-A, Greater Kailash-I
  New Delhi-110 048
  (Open Sundays)
  Tel : 641 2262
- B-40, Greater Kailash-I
  New Delhi-110 048
  Tel : 644 6847
- 96-E, Malcha Marg
  Diplomatic Enclave,
  Chanakyapuri
  New Delhi-110 021
  Tel : 301 5184
  Hotel Kanishka, Janpath
  New Delhi-110 001
  Tel : 332 4422
- 4/24, East Patel Nagar
  Opp. Siddhartha Icon.
  New Delhi-110 005
  Tel : 572 9746, 573 5442

**Woman's World International
Beauty Institute and
Shamute Free Beauty Institute
for Deaf and Dumb Girls**
M-86, Greater Kailash-I
New Delhi-110 048
Tel : 643 9434, 641 4891

**Women's World Beauty
Institute & Yoga Centre**
'Santushti', New Willington Camp
Opp. Hotel Samrat
New Delhi-110 021

Taj Khazana
Hotel Taj Mahal
1, Mansingh Road, New Delhi
Tel : 301 6162

**Shahnaz Herbal Range is
Also Available at :**

Central Cottage
Industries Emporiums
New Delhi · Bombay · Bangalore

Overseas :

Selfridges, London
a. Holland & Barette
b. Bluehurst
London. Salon
Paris
a. Theranol
b. Galeries Lafayette
Dubai, Salon
Abu Dhabi, Salon

Japan
Matsushita Trading Co. Ltd.,

Canada
Shahnaz Herbal

Reunion Island, Salon
Malaysia
Natural Remedies Sdn Bhd
Bangkok, Salon
Singapore, Salon
Yugoslavia
Sodaso
Czechoslovakia, Praha
Bahrain, Salon
Jashanmal

What every woman should do for herself and her family
What every mother should teach her daughters
What every husband, lover, father should know

Breast Self-Examination
Dr. Albert Milan   Illustrated

The lessons taught in this book are crucial to a woman's
well being and peace of mind... they may save her life.

"This book should be in the hands of every adult woman."
Dr. D.J. Jussawalla
Sr. Surgeon & Prof. of Oncology
Tata Memorial Hospital, Bombay

*"A life-saving little book on breast self-examination. The
technique is easy-to-learn and simple to practise."*
Dr. Edward F. Lewison, M.D.
Chief, Breast Clinic
Johns Hopkins Hospital, and
Assoc. Prof. of Surgery
Johns Hopkins School of Medicine, USA

"A concise, valuable book that will comfort as well as inform."
Publishers Weekly, USA

"A much needed manual for the layman..."
Dr. Clifford R. Wheeless, Jr.
Chief, Gynecology & Obstetrics
Union Memorial Hospital, and
Asst. Prof. Johns Hopkins School
of Medicine, USA

Available at all bookshops or by V.P.P.

**Orient
Paperbacks**
5A/8 Ansari Road, New Delhi-110 002